ADDISON WESLEY

Math
Makes Sense

7

Practice and Homework Book

Author Team

Ray Appel

Amy Lin

Peggy Morrow

Andrew Reeves

David Sufrin

PEARSON

Education
Canada

Elementary Math Team Leader
Anne-Marie Scullion

Publisher
Claire Burnett

Publishing Team
Lesley Haynes
Enid Haley
Tricia Carmichael
Winnie Siu
Stephanie Cox
Judy Wilson

Product Manager
Diane Wyman

Design
Word & Image Design Studio Inc.

Typesetting
Computer Composition of Canada Inc.

ISBN 0-321-24230-0

Printed and bound in USA.

21   17

Contents

Fractions and Decimals

UNIT 4

Data Management

UNIT 5

Measuring Perimeter and Area

UNIT 6

Patterning and Algebra

Probability

About

Math

Makes Sense 7

Practice and Homework Book

Welcome to *Addison Wesley Math Makes Sense 7*. These pages describe how this Practice and Homework Book can support your progress through the year.

Each unit offers the following features.

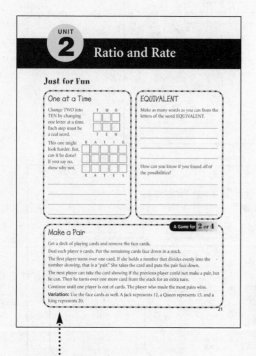

Skills You'll Need matches pages in the Student Book. A brief introduction and Examples refresh your skills, and Check questions let you reinforce these prerequisite skills.

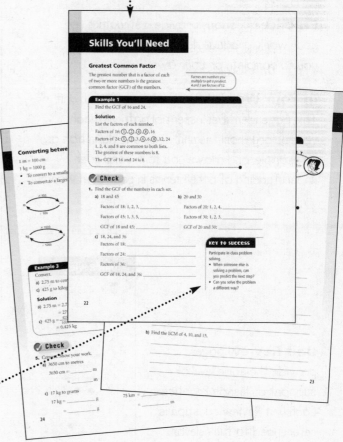

Just for Fun presents puzzles, games, or activities to help you warm up for the content to come. You may work with key words, numeracy skills, or creative and critical thinking skills.

Key to Success highlights ways you can develop your study skills, test-taking skills, and overall independence as a grade 7 student.

For each lesson of the Student Book, the workbook provides 3 to 4 pages of support.

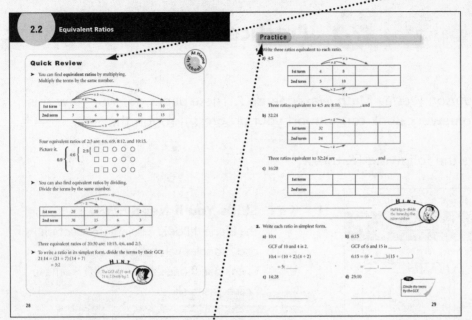

Quick Review covers the core concepts from the lesson. If used for homework, this Quick Review lets you bring just the Practice and Homework Book home.

Practice questions provide a structure for your work, gradually leaving more steps for you to complete on your own.

In Your Words helps to close off each unit. This page identifies essential mathematical vocabulary from the unit, gives one definition as an example, and allows you to record your understanding of other terms in your own words.

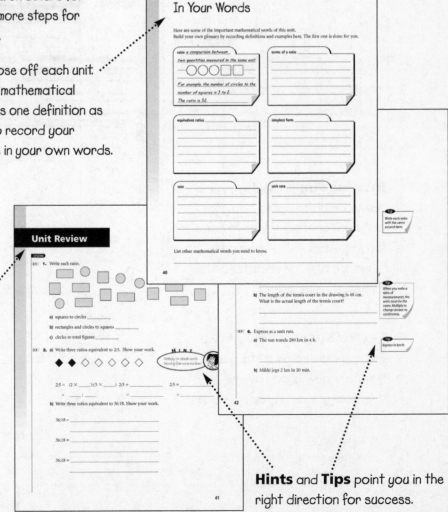

Unit Review pages provide the same level of support as lesson Practice. Each Unit Review question is referenced to the relevant lesson where related concepts are developed.

Hints and **Tips** point you in the right direction for success.

Just for Fun

Word Find

Can you find the following words in the puzzle below?

BASE   FORM   CUBE
MULTIPLE   EXPONENT

You can move in any direction to find the entire word.
A letter may be used for more than one word.
The first word is found for you.

M	F	O	R	M
N	E	N	O	U
T	A	S	P	L
U	B	X	E	T
C	E	L	P	I

Pattern Search

Choose a grid of any 4 squares in the calendar. What patterns do you see in the numbers?

May						
1	2	3	4	5	6	7
8	9	10	11	12	13	14
15	16	17	18	19	20	21
22	23	24	25	26	27	28
29	30	31				

_____

_____

_____

_____

_____

Variation: Choose a grid of any 9 squares or pick a different month and try again.

A Game for **2 or more**

Compose It!

Make as many words as you can from the letters of the word COMPOSITE.
The person who makes the greatest number of words in 1 min wins!

_____

_____

Skills You'll Need

Rounding

To round:

Look at the digit to the right of the place to which you are rounding.

Is this digit 5 or greater?

If it is, add 1 to the place digit.

If it is not, leave the place digit as it is.

Change all the digits to the right of the place digit to 0.

Example 1

a) Round 46 to the nearest ten.

b) Round 246 to the nearest hundred.

c) Round 8246 to the nearest thousand.

Solution

a)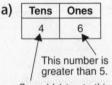

46 rounded to the nearest ten is 50.

b)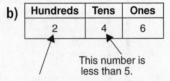

246 rounded to the nearest hundred is 200.

c)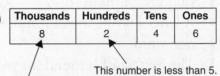

8246 rounded to the nearest thousand is 8000.

✔ Check

1. Match each original number to its rounded number. The first one is done for you.

Original Number	Rounded Number
25	50
57	30
23	60
52	20

2. Round to the nearest hundred.   **a)** 399 _____   **b)** 140 _____

3. Round to the nearest thousand.   **a)** 1001 _____   **b)** 3221 _____

Multiplying by 10, 100, 1000

To multiply a whole number:
* by 10, write 0 after the number.
* by 100, write 00 after the number.
* by 1000, write 000 after the number.

Example 2

Multiply.
a) 35×10 b) 22×100 c) 12×1000 d) 52×200

Solution

a) 35×10
   $= 350$

b) 22×100
   $= 2200$

c) 12×1000
   $= 12\ 000$

d) 52×200
   $= 104 \times 100$
   $= 10\ 400$

HINT
You can write 200 as 2×100.

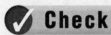 **Check**

4. How many zeros should you write after the number to get the product?

a) 23×10 _____   b) 758×1000 _____   c) 62×100 _____

5. Multiply.

a) 166×10

= _____

b) 990×100

= _____

c) 24×1000

= _____

d) 419×1000

= _____

e) 24×500

$= 24 \times 5 \times 100$

= _____

= _____

f) 12×400

= _____

= _____

= _____

3

Mental Math

There are many ways to calculate mentally.

- Look for 10s, or the nearest 10.
- Add or subtract in a different order.
- Separate a number into smaller parts to obtain friendly numbers.

Example 3

Use mental math.

a) 36×4 b) $403 + 55 - 4$ c) $305 + 498$

Solution

a) Separate 36 into 30 and 6:
$30 \times 4 + 6 \times 4$
$= 120 + 24$
$= 144$

b) Subtract first:
$55 - 4 = 51$
Then: $403 + 51 = 454$

c) $498 = 500 - 2$
Then: $305 + 500 - 2$
$= 803$

I have a different approach for part a.
I know double 35 is 70, and double that is 140. Then I added 4 to get $36 \times 4 = 144$.

 **Check**

6. Use mental math.
   a) $289 + 171 = 289 + $ _____ $ + 170$

      $= $ _____ $ + 170$

      $= $ _____

   b) 51×2

      $50 \times 2 = $ _____ $1 \times 2 = $ _____

      _____

7. Use mental math. Explain your strategy.

   a) $52 + 17 - 7 = $ _____

   b) $8 + 31 + 102 = $ _____

   c) $47 \times 2 = $ _____

   d) $65 \times 3 = $ _____

   e) $158 + 86 = $ _____

   f) $34 \times 25 \times 4 = $ _____

4

Divisibility Rules

A number is divisible by:

- 2 if the number is even
- 3 if the sum of the digits is divisible by 3
- 4 if the number represented by the last 2 digits is divisible by 4
- 5 if the last digit is 0 or 5
- 6 if the number is divisible by 2 and 3
- 8 if the number represented by the last 3 digits is divisible by 8
- 9 if the sum of the digits is divisible by 9
- 10 if the last digit is 0

Example 4

Which of these numbers is 344 divisible by? Explain.

a) 2   b) 5   c) 3   d) 4

Solution

a) 344 is divisible by 2 because 344 is an even number.

b) The last digit is not 0 or 5, so 344 is not divisible by 5.

c) The sum of the digits is: $3 + 4 + 4 = 11$; 11 is not divisible by 3, so 344 is not divisible by 3.

d) The number represented by the last 2 digits is 44. 44 is divisible by 4, so 344 is divisible by 4.

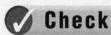 **Check**

8. Complete each sentence.

   a) 220 is divisible by 2, since it is _____.

   b) 220 is divisible by 4, since the number represented by its last 2 digits is divisible by _____.

   c) 220 is divisible by 5, since _____.

9. Is 2925 divisible by each number? Explain.

   a) 6   2925 is not even, so it is not divisible by 2 or by _____.

   b) 9   The sum of the digits of 2925 is: _____

   _____

   c) 10   The last digit of 2925 is not 0, so _____

Quick Review

At Home At School

Numbers you read could be exact numbers or estimates.
Words like *about*, *approximately*, and *or so* help you to know when a number is an estimate.

> **Flood Destroys
> 152 Homes**
> Today, a flood has left 326 people homeless.
>
> In the past 3 decades or so, there have been approximately a dozen floods in the same area.
>
> Each flood has left about 300 people homeless.

In the article, 152 and 326 are exact numbers.
The numbers 3, dozen, and 300 are estimates.

About how many people have been left homeless by floods in the past 3 decades?

Tip
The "about" in the question means you can estimate the answer.

To find the total number of people left homeless by floods in the past 3 decades, multiply the number of floods by the number of people left homeless in each flood.

Round "dozen" to 10.
There have been about 10 floods.
Multiply: $300 \times 10 = 3000$

The floods have left about 3000 people homeless in the past 3 decades.

- When you can handle the numbers easily, use mental math.
- When the problem has too many steps, use pencil and paper.
- When an approximate answer is appropriate and to check reasonableness, estimate.
- When you need a more accurate answer and the numbers are large, use a calculator.

Practice

1. Write "estimate" or "exact" for each number.

   a) Dinosaurs disappeared about 65 million years ago. _____

   b) In the race, 62 people swam to the finish line. _____

   c) The students sold 211 bagels in the Bake Sale last week. _____

   d) Approximately 50 000 people ran in the Sun Run in Vancouver this year.

   _____

6

2. Match the estimate to the exact number. The first one is done for you.

Estimate	Exact Number
about 400	5254.31
over $5000	398
close to 100 gold bricks	9833
approximately 10 000 boxes	91

3. Use mental math to find each answer.

a) 99 + 21 = _____

b) 1444 × 20 = _____

c) 4882 ÷ 2 = _____

d) 199 − 89 = _____

4. Use pencil and paper to find each answer.

a) 76 × 32 = _____

b) 244 + 843 = _____

c) 467 × 233 = _____

d) 5699 − 3511 = _____

5. There are 1776 steps to the top of the CN Tower in Toronto.
Each year, approximately 8000 people climb those steps to raise money for charity.
They usually raise over $500 000.

a) List 2 estimates. _____

b) List 1 exact number. _____

c) About how much does each person raise by climbing the CN Tower?

_____

Each person raises about _____ each year.

d) Suppose Michael climbs 8 steps in approximately 4 s.
About how many minutes would Michael take
to climb to the top of the CN Tower?

HINT
You can round 1776 to 1800 first.

Michael would take about _____ min to climb to the top of the CN Tower.

Quick Review

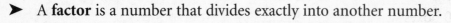
➤ A **factor** is a number that divides exactly into another number.

A **prime number** has only 2 factors, itself and 1.
11 is a prime number. Its only factors are 11 and 1.

A **composite number** has more than 2 factors.
12 is a composite number. Its factors are 1, 2, 3, 4, 6, and 12.

➤ You can use a Venn diagram to find the
greatest common factor (GCF) of 15 and 20.
Use the divisibility rules to sort the factors
of 15 and 20.
Place all the common factors of 15 and 20
in the overlapping region.
The greatest number in the overlapping
region is 5, so the GCF of 15 and 20 is 5.

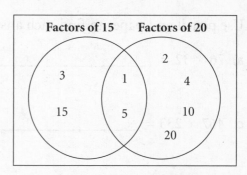

➤ One way to find the **lowest common multiple**
(LCM) of 6 and 9 is by using a 100 chart.
The multiples of 6 are shaded.
The multiples of 9 are underlined.
The common multiples are underlined
and shaded.
You can see that the LCM of 6 and 9 is 18.

1	2	3	4	5	6	7	8	9	10
11	12	13	14	15	16	17	18	19	20
21	22	23	24	25	26	27	28	29	30
31	32	33	34	35	36	37	38	39	40
41	42	43	44	45	46	47	48	49	50
51	52	53	54	55	56	57	58	59	60
61	62	63	64	65	66	67	68	69	70
71	72	73	74	75	76	77	78	79	80
81	82	83	84	85	86	87	88	89	90
91	92	93	94	95	96	97	98	99	100

Practice

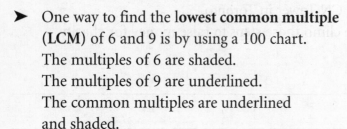

1. Complete the list of factors of each number.

a) 14
   1, 2, _____, _____

b) 16
   1, 2, _____, _____, _____

c) 42
   1, 2, 3, 6, 7, ____, ____, ____

HINT

When you look for
factors, look for pairs
of numbers.

2. a) Skip count to find the missing multiples.

Then circle the common multiples.

3: 3, 6, 9, 12, _____, _____, _____, _____, _____

6: 6, 12, 18, _____, _____, _____, _____, _____

b) The LCM of 3 and 6 is _____.

3. a) Complete the Venn diagram.

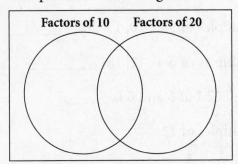

b) The GCF of 10 and 20 is _____.

4. a) Complete the Venn diagram.

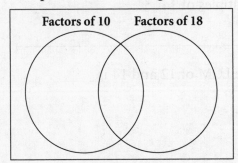

b) The GCF of 10 and 18 is _____.

5. Shade the multiples of 6. Underline the multiples of 10.

1	2	3	4	5	6	7	8	9	10
11	12	13	14	15	16	17	18	19	20
21	22	23	24	25	26	27	28	29	30
31	32	33	34	35	36	37	38	39	40
41	42	43	44	45	46	47	48	49	50
51	52	53	54	55	56	57	58	59	60
61	62	63	64	65	66	67	68	69	70
71	72	73	74	75	76	77	78	79	80
81	82	83	84	85	86	87	88	89	90
91	92	93	94	95	96	97	98	99	100

The LCM of 6 and 10 is _____.

6. **a)** Factors of 4: 1, 2, 4

Factors of 8: 1, 2, 4, 8

The GCF of 4 and 8 is _____.

b) Factors of 9: 1, 3, _____

Factors of 20: 1, 2, 4, 5, _____

The GCF of 9 and 20 is _____.

c) Factors of 12: _____

Factors of 30: _____

The GCF of 12 and 30 is _____.

d) Factors of 7: _____

Factors of 13: _____

The GCF of 7 and 13 is _____.

7. **a)** Multiples of 4: 4, 8, 12, 16, 20, ...

Multiples of 8: 8, 16, 24, 32, 40, ...

The LCM of 4 and 8 is _____.

b) Multiples of 5: 5, 10, 15, 20, _____

Multiples of 6: 6, 12, 18, _____

The LCM of 5 and 6 is _____.

c) Multiples of 10:

_____

Multiples of 12:

_____

The LCM of 10 and 12 is _____.

d) Multiples of 12:

_____

Multiples of 14:

_____

The LCM of 12 and 14 is _____.

8. Allison and Sameer are on the cross-country team.
Allison runs every 3 days starting on September 3.
Sameer runs every 5 days starting on September 5.

a) On what day do they run together for the first time?

Allison runs on days _____

Sameer runs on days _____

The first day they run together is September _____.

b) When will they run together again?
Explain how you know.

_____

_____

_____

_____

H I N T

The first day that Allison and Sameer run together is the LCM of 3 and 5.

Quick Review

➤ When a number is multiplied by itself, the product is a **square number**.

You can get 16 by multiplying 4 by itself.

$16 = 4 \times 4$

You can write: $4 \times 4 = 4^2$

You can say: 4 squared is 16.

16 is a square number.

You can model 16 as a square number geometrically.

4 units

4 units

➤ Finding a **square root** is the inverse operation of squaring a number.

$4 \times 4 = 16$ $\qquad \sqrt{16} = \sqrt{4^2}$

So, $4^2 = 16$ $\qquad\qquad\qquad = 4$

The side length of the square is $\sqrt{16}$, or 4 units.
You can say: A **square root** of 16 is 4.

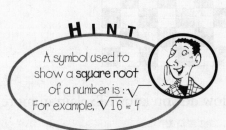

HINT

A symbol used to show a **square root** of a number is : $\sqrt{}$
For example, $\sqrt{16} = 4$

Practice

1. Match all three columns. The first one is done for you.

$2 \times 2 = 4$	5^2	$\sqrt{16} = 4$
$4 \times 4 = 16$	20^2	$\sqrt{4} = 2$
$10 \times 10 = 100$	10^2	$\sqrt{25} = 5$
$5 \times 5 = 25$	2^2	$\sqrt{64} = 8$
$20 \times 20 = 400$	8^2	$\sqrt{400} = 20$
$8 \times 8 = 64$	4^2	$\sqrt{100} = 10$

2. Find the square of each number. The first one is done for you.

a) 3 $3 \times 3 = 9$ The square of 3 is 9.

b) 11 $11 \times 11 =$ _____   The square of 11 is _____.

c) 5   _____ $\times$ _____ = _____   The square of _____ is _____.

d) 14 _____

3. True or False? Explain your answers.

a) A square grid with area 4 is 2×2 square units. True; _____

b) A square grid with area 8 is 4×2 square units. _____

c) A square grid with area 10 000 is 100×100 square units. _____

4. How many small squares are there on the checker board?

How do you know? Explain in more than one way.

_____

_____

_____

_____

5. Draw a square on each grid to show each square number.

a) 36   **b)** 100   **c)** 81

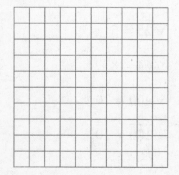 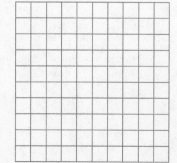 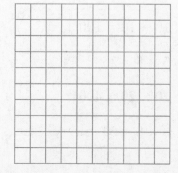

6. a) Write the next 4 square numbers: 1, _____, _____, _____, _____

b) Draw a diagram to find a square root of each number you wrote in part a.

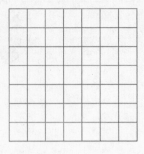

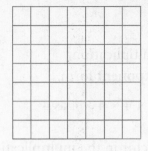

_____

_____

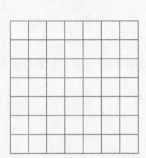

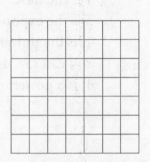

_____

_____

7. Find each square root. Use a calculator if necessary.

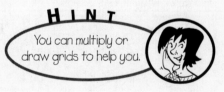

H I N T

You can multiply or draw grids to help you.

a) $\sqrt{36} =$ _____

b) $\sqrt{10\ 000} =$ _____

c) $\sqrt{2025} =$ _____

d) $\sqrt{324} =$ _____

8. Workers are going to build a fence around a square playground. The area of the playground is 225 m².

a) Find the length of a side of the playground.

$\sqrt{225} = 15$ The side length is _____.

b) How much fencing is needed to go around the playground?

_____

c) The fencing comes in pieces that are each 5 m long. How many pieces of fencing are needed? Show your work.

_____

_____

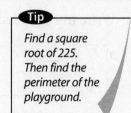

Tip

Find a square root of 225. Then find the perimeter of the playground.

Quick Review

When a number is repeated in multiplication,
you can write the expression in **exponent** form.

For example, you can write $4 \times 4 \times 4 \times 4 \times 4$ as 4^5.
The exponent is 5.
It shows how many times 4 is a factor in the multiplication.

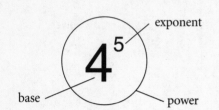

4 is the **base**.
5 is the **exponent**.
4^5 is the **power**.
You can say: 4 to the power of 5, or 4 to the 5th
4^5 is a power of 4.

Practice

1. Match the power to the base. The first one is done for you.

Power	Base
2^4	6
5^2	5
6^2	10
10^3	2

2. Write in expanded form.

a) $8^6 = $ _____ $\times$ _____ $\times$ _____ $\times$ _____ $\times$ _____ $\times$ _____

b) $3^5 = $ _____

c) $2^7 = $ _____

d) $5^2 = $ _____

e) $9^9 = $ _____

f) $6^4 = $ _____

3. Draw a picture for each power. Label each drawing.

a) 2^3 b) 5^2 c) 7^3

4. Match the expanded form to the exponent form.

Expanded Form	Exponent Form
$4 \times 4 \times 4$	5^4
$5 \times 5 \times 5 \times 5$	4^3
$3 \times 3 \times 3 \times 3$	3^4
$10 \times 10 \times 10 \times 10 \times 10$	1^2
1×1	10^5

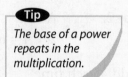

Tip

The base of a power repeats in the multiplication.

5. Write in exponent form and in standard form.

a) $3 \times 3 = 3^2$

= _____

b) $5 \times 5 \times 5 = 5^3$

= _____

c) $7 \times 7 \times 7 \times 7 =$ _____

= _____

d) $2 \times 2 \times 2 \times 2 \times 2 =$ _____

= _____

6. Complete the table.

Exponent Form	Perfect Square?	Perfect Cube?	Expanded Form	Standard Form
	No		$4 \times 4 \times 4$	
10^3				1000
	Yes			36
		No	7×7	

7. a) Simplify.

$1^3 =$ _____ $1^{12} =$ _____ $1^7 =$ _____ $1^{23} =$ _____

b) What do you notice? Explain. _____

_____

Quick Review

A pattern rule describes a pattern of numbers.
You can use a pattern rule to find the next 3 numbers in this pattern.

2, 6, 10, 14, 18, ...

Look at the starting number and how the pattern continues.

Start at 2.   Add 4.   Add 4.   Add 4.   Add 4, and so on.
                $2 + 4 = 6$ $6 + 4 = 10$ $10 + 4 = 14$ $14 + 4 = 18$

You add 4 each time.

The next 3 numbers are: $18 + 4 = 22$, $22 + 4 = 26$, $26 + 4 = 30$

Practice

1. Write the next 3 terms in each pattern.

Tip

Find the difference between two consecutive terms.

   a) Add 2: 6, 8, 10, 12, _____, _____, _____

   b) Add 3: 10, 13, 16, _____, _____, _____

   c) Add 4: 3, 7, 11, 15, _____, _____, _____

   d) Subtract 10: 180, 170, 160, 150, _____, _____, _____

   e) Multiply by 2: 7, 14, 28, _____, _____, _____

2. True or False? If the pattern rule is false, write a correct rule.

   a) 1, 2, 3, 4, 5, ... Start at 1. Add 1 each time. _____

   b) 2, 4, 6, 8, 10, ... Start at 2. Add 4 each time. _____

   c) 5, 11, 17, 23, 29, ... Start at 5. Add 6 each time. _____

   d) 10, 9, 8, 7, ... Start at 10. Add 1 each time. _____

   e) 2, 4, 8, 16, ... Start at 2. Multiply by 2 each time. _____

   f) 30, 25, 20, 15, ... Start at 15. Add 5 each time. _____

3. Match the number pattern to the pattern rule.
Complete the pattern rules.

Number Pattern	Pattern Rule
3, 6, 9, 12, ...	Start at _____. List the square numbers starting at 1.
55, 44, 33, 22, 11, ...	Start at _____. Add 3 each time.
1, 4, 9, 16, 25, ...	Start at _____. Subtract 11 each time.
5, 10, 15, 20, ...	Start at _____. Add 5 each time.

4. **a)** Sketch the next 3 pictures in the pattern.

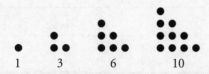

b) Write a pattern rule. _____

_____

c) Write the next 3 numbers in the pattern: 1, 3, 6, 10, _____, _____, _____

5. **a)** Sketch the next 3 pictures in the pattern.

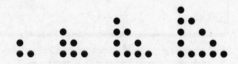

b) Write a pattern rule. _____

_____

c) Write the next 3 numbers in the pattern: 3, 6, 9, 12, _____, _____, _____

6. Describe each pattern in words.

a) 13, 23, 33, 43, ... _____

b) 3, 6, 12, 24, ... _____

c) 168, 84, 42, 21, ... _____

d) 100, 1000, 10 000, 100 000, ... _____

In Your Words

Here are some of the important mathematical words of this unit.
Build your own glossary by recording definitions and examples here. The first one is done for you.

factor _a number that divides exactly into another number_
For example, the factors of 50 are
1, 2, 5, 10, 25, and 50.

power

square number

square root

lowest common multiple (LCM)

greatest common factor (GCF)

List other mathematical words you need to know.

Unit Review

1.1   **1.** Use mental math to find each answer.

     a) 48 + 52 = _____

     b) 2000 × 16 = _____

     c) 158 + 201 + 544 = _____

     d) 499 – 22 = _____

   2. a) Read the following article.

> Yesterday, 1893 people took the
> Polar Bear Plunge.
> They took turns running into water
> even though it was -10°C outside!
> Every year, about 2000 people take
> part in this freezing cold
> challenge.
> This year, the oldest person was 87.
> The average age of participants over
> the last decade or so has been
> about 25.

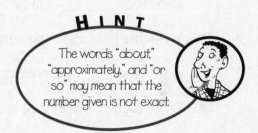

HINT

The words "about," "approximately," and "or so" may mean that the number given is not exact.

     b) List 3 estimates from the article. _____

     c) List 3 exact numbers from the article. _____

1.2   **3. a)** Complete the Venn diagram.   **b)** The GCF of 12 and 24 is _____.

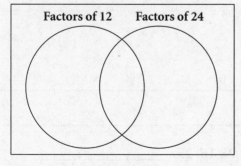

Factors of 12   Factors of 24

   4. a) Skip count to find the missing numbers.
       Then circle the common multiples.

     4:    4,   8,   12,   16, _____, _____, _____, _____, _____

     6:    6,   12,   18,   24, _____, _____, _____, _____, _____

     b) The LCM of 4 and 6 is _____.

1.3 **5.** Write the side length of each square.

a) _____
b) _____
c) _____

6. Find each square root.
Multiply or draw squares to help you.

a) $\sqrt{100}$ = _____
b) $\sqrt{144}$ = _____
c) $\sqrt{40\ 000}$ = _____
d) $\sqrt{225}$ = _____

1.4 **7.** Write the base and exponent of each power.

a) 7^3: base: _____ exponent: _____
b) 3^8: base: _____ exponent: _____

8. Write each power in expanded form and in standard form.

a) 9^2 = _____

 = _____

b) 10^3 = _____

 = _____

c) 3^4 = _____

 = _____

d) 5^5 = _____

 = _____

1.5 **9.** a) Sketch the next 3 pictures in the pattern.

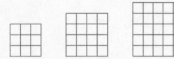

b) Write a pattern rule. _____

_____

c) Write the next 3 numbers in the pattern: 9, 16, 25, _____, _____, _____

10. Describe each pattern in words. Then write the next 3 terms.

a) 10, 20, 30, 40, ... _____

b) 98, 96, 94, 92, ... _____

c) 25, 50, 100, 200, ... _____

UNIT 2 — Ratio and Rate

Just for Fun

One at a Time

Change TWO into TEN by changing one letter at a time. Each step must be a real word.

T W O
□ □ □
□ □
T E N

This one might look harder. But, can it be done? If you say no, show why not.

R A T I O
□ □ □ □ □
□ □ □ □ □
□ □ □ □ □
R A T E S

_____
_____
_____
_____

EQUIVALENT

Make as many words as you can from the letters of the word EQUIVALENT.

_____
_____
_____
_____

How can you know if you found *all* of the possibilities?

_____
_____
_____

Make a Pair

A Game for 2 or 4

Get a deck of playing cards and remove the face cards.

Deal each player 6 cards. Put the remaining cards face down in a stack.

The first player turns over one card. If she holds a number that divides evenly into the number showing, that is a "pair." She takes the card and puts the pair face down.

The next player can take the card showing if the previous player could not make a pair, but he can. Then he turns over one more card from the stack for an extra turn.

Continue until one player is out of cards. The player who made the most pairs wins.

Variation: Use the face cards as well. A jack represents 12, a Queen represents 15, and a King represents 20.

21

Skills You'll Need

Greatest Common Factor

The greatest number that is a factor of each of two or more numbers is the greatest common factor (GCF) of the numbers.

> Factors are numbers you multiply to get a product. 4 and 3 are factors of 12.

Example 1

Find the GCF of 16 and 24.

Solution

List the factors of each number.

Factors of 16: ①,②,④,⑧,16

Factors of 24: ①,②,3,④,6,⑧,12, 24

1, 2, 4, and 8 are common to both lists.
The greatest of these numbers is 8.

The GCF of 16 and 24 is 8.

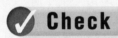

Check

1. Find the GCF of the numbers in each set.

a) 18 and 45

Factors of 18: 1, 2, 3, _____

Factors of 45: 1, 3, 5, _____

GCF of 18 and 45: _____

b) 20 and 30

Factors of 20: 1, 2, 4, _____

Factors of 30: 1, 2, 3, _____

GCF of 20 and 30: _____

c) 18, 24, and 36

Factors of 18: _____

Factors of 24: _____

Factors of 36: _____

GCF of 18, 24, and 36: _____

Lowest Common Multiple

The lowest common multiple (LCM) is the least number that is a multiple of each number in a set of numbers.

Example 2

Find the LCM of 8, 9, and 12.

Solution

List the multiples of each number until you find a match.
Start with the greatest number.

Multiples of 12:   12, 24, 36, 48, 60, (72), ...

Multiples of 9:   9, 18, 27, 36, 45, 54, 63, (72), ...

Multiples of 8:   8, 16, 24, 32, 40, 48, 56, 64, (72), ...

The LCM of 8, 9, and 12 is 72.

H I N T

You can find the multiples of a number by skip counting.

✓ Check

2. Use skip counting to find the first 5 multiples of each number.

a) 6:   6, 12, 18, _____, _____

b) 11:   11, 22, _____, _____, _____

c) 25:   25, _____, _____, _____, _____

3. Find the LCM of 15 and 25.

Multiples of 15: _____

Multiples of 25: _____

LCM of 15 and 25: _____

4. a) Find the LCM of 6 and 14.

_____

_____

_____

b) Find the LCM of 4, 10, and 15.

_____

_____

_____

_____

Converting between Metric Units

1 m = 100 cm   1 km = 1000 m

1 kg = 1000 g   1 L = 1000 mL

- To convert to a smaller unit, multiply.
- To convert to a larger unit, divide.

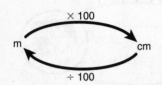
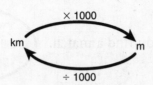

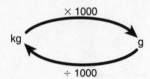
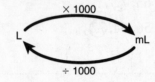

> When I multiply a number by 100, the decimal point moves 2 places to the right. When I divide by 1000, the decimal point moves 3 places to the left.

Example 3

Convert.

a) 2.75 m to centimetres   b) 2450 m to kilometres

c) 425 g to kilograms   d) 3.4 L to millilitres

Solution

a) 2.75 m = 2.75 × 100 cm   b) 2450 m = $\frac{2450}{1000}$ km

       = 275 cm   = 2.45 km

c) 425 g = $\frac{425}{1000}$ kg   d) 3.4 L = 3.4 × 1000 mL

       = 0.425 kg   = 3400 mL

✓ Check

5. Convert. Show your work.

a) 3650 cm to metres   b) 5260 mL to litres

    3650 cm = _____ m   5260 mL = _____ L

           = _____ m   = _____ L

c) 17 kg to grams   d) 75 km to metres

    17 kg = _____ g   75 km = _____ m

         = _____ g   = _____ m

Quick Review

There are 6 circles and 8 squares.

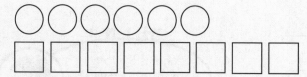

Here are some ways you can use a **ratio** to compare the figures.

➤ **Part-to-Whole Ratio**
- The ratio of circles to all of the figures is 6 to 14 or 6:14.
- The ratio of squares to all of the figures is 8 to 14 or 8:14.

➤ **Part-to-Part Ratio**
- The ratio of circles to squares is 6 to 8 or 6:8.
  6 and 8 are the **terms** of this ratio.
- The ratio of squares to circles is 8 to 6 or 8:6.
  8 is the **first term** and 6 is the **second term** of this ratio.

Practice

1. Write each ratio.

   a) cars to vans   b) footballs to baseballs   c) bananas to fruit

   _____ : _____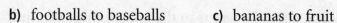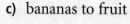

2. Write each ratio.

   a) turtles to total animals _____ : _____

   b) rabbits to turtles _____

   c) rabbits to total animals _____

   d) turtles to rabbits _____

HINT

What is the total number of rabbits? of turtles? of animals?

3. Franny has only dimes and quarters in her pocket.
The ratio of dimes to total coins is 8 to 11.

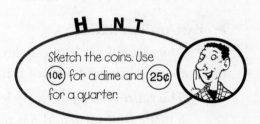

HINT

Sketch the coins. Use 10¢ for a dime and 25¢ for a quarter.

   a) How many quarters might be in Franny's pocket? _____

   b) What is the ratio of dimes to quarters? _____

   c) What is the ratio of quarters to the total number of coins? _____

4. Make a sketch to show that the ratio of triangles to circles is 6:13.
Write 3 ratios to compare the figures.

   a) circles to triangles _____

   b) circles to total figures _____

   c) triangles to total figures _____

5. Write each ratio.

    a) hexagons to pentagons _____

    b) pentagons to hexagons _____

    c) hexagons to total figures _____

    d) pentagons to total figures _____

    e) black figures to white figures _____

    f) white figures to total figures _____

6. What are being compared in each ratio?

    a) 7:9   _____ to total vegetables

    b) 2:7   tomatoes to _____

    c) 7:2   _____ to _____

    d) 9:2   _____ to _____

    e) 2:9   _____ to _____

7. A pencil case contains 7 yellow, 3 red, 1 black, and 5 green crayons.
    a) Write each ratio.

        • red:green _____   • yellow:red _____

        • black: total crayons _____   • yellow:total crayons _____

    b) What is the ratio of yellow and red crayons to total crayons? _____

    c) What is the ratio of green crayons to black and red crayons? _____

    d) Suppose 2 yellow and 2 green crayons are lost.
        Rewrite the ratios in part a.

        • red:green _____   • yellow:red _____

        • black:total crayons _____   • yellow:total crayons _____

Quick Review

➤ You can find **equivalent ratios** by multiplying.
Multiply the terms by the same number.

	×2	×3	×4	×5
1st term	2	4	6	8	10
2nd term	3	6	9	12	15

Four equivalent ratios of 2:3 are: 4:6, 6:9, 8:12, and 10:15.

Picture it.

6:9 { 4:6 { 2:3 { □ □ ○ ○ ○
□ □ ○ ○ ○
□ □ ○ ○ ○

➤ You can also find equivalent ratios by dividing.
Divide the terms by the same number.

	÷10	÷5	÷2	
1st term	20	10	4	2
2nd term	30	15	6	3

Three equivalent ratios of 20:30 are: 10:15, 4:6, and 2:3.

➤ To write a ratio in its simplest form, divide the terms by their GCF.
21:14 = (21 ÷ 7):(14 ÷ 7)
= 3:2

HINT

The GCF of 21 and 14 is 7. Divide by 7.

Practice

1. Write three ratios equivalent to each ratio.

a) 4:5

×3
×2

1st term	4	8		
2nd term	5	10		

×2
×3

Three ratios equivalent to 4:5 are 8:10, _____, and _____.

b) 32:24

÷2

1st term	32			
2nd term	24			

÷2

Three ratios equivalent to 32:24 are _____, _____, and _____.

c) 16:28

1st term				
2nd term				

_____

_____

HINT

Multiply or divide the terms by the same number.

2. Write each ratio in simplest form.

a) 10:4

GCF of 10 and 4 is 2.

10:4 = (10 ÷ 2):(4 ÷ 2)

= 5: _____

b) 6:15

GCF of 6 and 15 is _____.

6:15 = (6 ÷ _____):(15 ÷ _____)

= _____ : _____

c) 14:28

d) 25:10

Tip

Divide the terms by the GCF.

_____   _____

3. a) Match the pairs of equivalent ratios.

    i)   5:6   1:2

          18:3   15:18

           9:18   8:40

           4:20   6:1

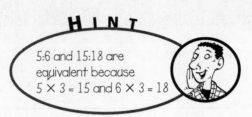

HINT

5:6 and 15:18 are equivalent because 5 × 3 = 15 and 6 × 3 = 18

    ii)   1:8   1:9

          3:27   1:3

         12:36   9:1

         18:2   2:16

b) How do you know that 12:36 and 1:3 are equivalent?

_____

_____

4. The ratio of cats to dogs at the animal shelter is 4 to 5.
How many cats could there be? How many dogs?
Write six different answers.

4 cats and 5 dogs   8 cats and _____ dogs

_____ cats and _____ dogs   _____

_____   _____

Tip

Multiply each term by the same number.

5. The length-to-width ratio of Colby's poster is 3:2.
The poster is 90 cm long. How wide is it?

HINT

Find a ratio equivalent to 3:2 in which the first term is 90.

$$\times 30$$
$$3:2 = 90:$$
$$\times 30$$

The poster is _____ cm wide.

Quick Review

You can use equivalent ratios to compare ratios.

Joe and Petra make orange punches with different ratios of crystals to water.

Joe makes orange punch with 4 scoops of crystals and 6 cups of water.

Petra makes orange punch with 3 scoops of crystals and 5 cups of water.

To find out whose orange punch is stronger,
- Write each mixture as a ratio.
- Write each ratio with the same second term.
- Compare the first terms.

HINT

A quick way to do this is to find the LCM of the second terms.

Joe	Petra
4:6	3:5

The LCM of 6 and 5 is 30.

Use equivalent ratios.

$4:6 = (4 \times 5):(6 \times 5)$
   $= 20:30$

$3:5 = (3 \times 6):(5 \times 6)$
   $= 18:30$

Joe uses 20 scoops of crystals to 30 cups of water.

Petra uses 18 scoops of crystals to 30 cups of water.

$20 > 18$, so Joe's orange punch is stronger.

31

Practice

1. Which mixture is stronger: A or B? Show your work.

Mixture A: _____ scoop of powder

to _____ cups of water.

Write each mixture as a ratio.

Write each ratio with the same second term.

Mixture B: _____ scoops of powder

to _____ cups of water.

A _____ :2   B 2: _____

A _____ :10   B _____

---

2. Two cages contain white mice and brown mice.
   In one cage, the ratio of white mice to brown mice is 2:3.
   In the other cage, the ratio is 3:1.
   The cages contain the same number of mice.

   HINT
   Multiply to find equivalent ratios. Add to find the total numbers of mice. Keep going until you get two totals that match.

   a) What could the total number of mice be?

Cage A		
White	Brown	Total
2	3	5
4	6	10
6		

Cage B		
White	Brown	Total
3	1	
6		

The number of mice in each cage could be _____.

The total number of mice could be _____.

   b) Which cage contains more white mice?

Number of white mice in A: _____   Number of white mice in B: _____

Cage _____ contains more white mice.

3.

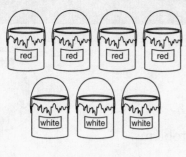

A   B

The red paint and white paint in each picture will be mixed.

Tip

Use the LCM of the second terms to write equivalent ratios.

Write the ratio of red paint to white paint.   A _____   B _____

Write each ratio with the same second term. A _____   B _____

Compare the first terms. _____

Which mixture will give a darker shade of red? _____

4. The ratio of computers to students at Jan's school is 3:5.
The ratio of computers to students at Karl's school is 2:3.
Both schools have the same number of students.
Which school has more computers? Show your work.

H I N T

Think about equivalent ratios.

Jan's School
      3:5

= (3 × 3):(5 × _____)

= _____ : _____

_____ computers to _____ students

Karl's School
      2:3

= (2 × 5):(3 × _____)

= _____ : _____

_____ computers to _____ students

_____ school has more computers.

5. Hamid jogs 5 laps in 6 min.
Amelia jogs 8 laps in 11 min.
Which person jogs faster? Show your work.

Quick Review

You can use diagrams and tables to model and solve ratio problems.

➤ A scale drawing of a patio uses a scale of 1 cm to represent 40 cm.
On the drawing, the patio is 14 cm long.
To find the actual length of the patio, you can draw a diagram.

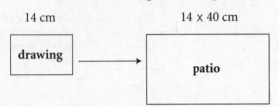

14 cm   14 × 40 cm

drawing ⟶   patio

HINT

To convert centimetres to metres, divide by 100. To divide by 100, move the decimal point 2 places to the left.

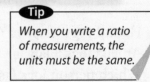

Each 1 cm in the drawing represents 40 cm.
So, the length of the patio is 14 × 40 cm = 560 cm

$$= \frac{560}{100} \text{ m}$$

$$= 5.6 \text{ m}$$

➤ The ratio of oil to vinegar for a salad dressing is 50 mL of oil to 15 mL of vinegar.
To find how much oil is needed for 75 mL of vinegar, you can make a table.

Oil (mL)	50	100	150	200	250
Vinegar (mL)	15	30	45	60	75

Multiply 50 and 15 by the same number to find equivalent ratios.

The table shows 250 mL of oil would be needed for 75 mL of vinegar.

Practice

1. Dexter is making a model of the CN Tower.
He uses a scale of 4 cm to 10 m.

   Tip
   When you write a ratio of measurements, the units must be the same.

   a) What is the ratio of the height of the model to
   the actual height of the tower?

   10 m = 10 × 100 cm   Multiply by 100 to change metres to centimetres.

   4 cm: _____ cm   Write the new ratio.

   = (4 cm ÷ _____):(_____ cm ÷ _____)   Divide each term by the GCF of the terms.

   = 1: _____   Write the ratio in simplest form.

   Each 1 cm of the model represents _____ of the tower.

b) The CN Tower is 553 m tall. How tall will the model be?

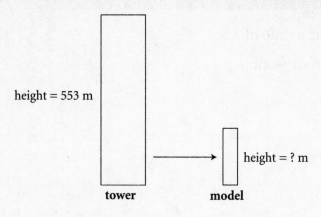

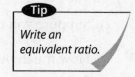

Tip

Draw a diagram.

height = 553 m

tower

height = ? m

model

553 m = 553 × _____ cm

= _____ cm

1 cm of the model represents _____ of the tower.

Height of model = _____ cm ÷ _____

= _____

2. This table shows the quantities of sugar and water needed for a hummingbird feeder.

Sugar (mL)	4	8	12	16		
Water (mL)	16	32	48	64		

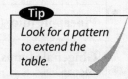

Tip

Look for a pattern to extend the table.

a) How much sugar is needed for 96 mL of water?

_____

b) How much water is needed for 10 mL of sugar?

4:16 = 1: _____

= 10: _____

Tip

Write an equivalent ratio.

_____

c) A hummingbird feeder contains a total of 60 mL of sugar and water.

What is the volume of sugar in the feeder? _____

What is the volume of water in the feeder? _____

3. Alberta makes a scale drawing of her bedroom.
She uses a scale of 3 cm to represent 5 m.
Alberta's friend Patrick says she is using a ratio of 3:5.

a) What ratio is Alberta using? Show your work.

_____

b) What mistake did Patrick make?

_____

_____

4. This table shows the quantities of juice and ginger ale needed to make fruit punch.

Orange juice (cups)	3	6	9		
Pineapple juice (cups)	1	2	3		
Ginger ale (cups)	4	8	12		
Amount of punch (L)	2	4	6		

Tip
Think of a pattern.

a) Write the next two numbers in each row of the table.

b) What is the ratio of orange juice to pineapple juice? _____

c) Suppose you use 15 cups of orange juice.

How much punch will you get? _____

d) Suppose you use 16 cups of juice in total.

How much punch will you get? _____

e) How much of each ingredient will you need to make 20 L of punch?

H I N T

20 is 2 times 10.

_____

_____

_____

Quick Review

➤ A **rate** is a comparison of two quantities measured in different units.

Leo types 180 words in 3 min.
180 words in 3 min is a **rate**.

This means Leo types 60 words in 1 min.
Leo's rate of typing is 60 words per minute.
You can write this as 60 words/min.

60 words/min is a **unit rate**.
It compares a quantity (60 words) to 1 unit (1 min).

➤ To find a unit rate, you can use a diagram, a table, or a graph.
In 3 min, Leo types 180 words.
In 1 min, Leo types 60 words.

A Diagram

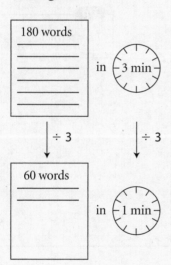

A Table

	÷ 3 →		
Minutes	3	2	1
Words	180	120	60
		÷ 3 →	

A Graph

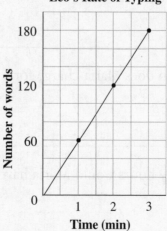

Leo's Rate of Typing

Practice

1. Express as a unit rate.

   a) Serena walks 4 km in 1 h. _____

   b) Sanjit reads 3 books in 1 week. _____

   c) The tap drips 25 drops in 1 min. _____

2. Express as a unit rate. Show your work.
   a) Betty drives her car 150 km in 2 h.

   150 km ÷ 2 = _____ km

   Betty's average driving speed is _____ km/h.

   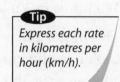
   Tip
   Express each rate in kilometres per hour (km/h).

   b) The helicopter travels 180 km in 3 h.

   _____

   _____

   c) Gerald walks 1 km in 15 min.

Distance (km)	1	2		
Time (min)	15	30		

   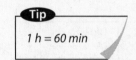
   Tip
   1 h = 60 min

   Gerald's rate of walking is _____ km/h.

3. Maria charges $15 for 3 hours of babysitting.
   a) What is Maria's rate per hour?

   _____

   b) How much does Maria charge for 5 hours of babysitting?

   _____

   c) How many hours would Maria have to babysit to earn $50?

   Maria has to babysit _____ to earn $50.

38

4. The graph shows the distance a freight train travels in 3 h.

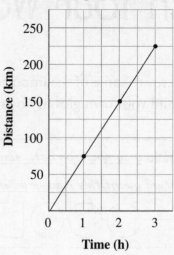

How a Freight Train Travels

a) How far does the train travel in 1 h?

_____

b) What is the average speed of the train?

_____

5. Frozen fruit bars cost $3.95 for 5 bars.
Find how many you can buy with $12. Show your work.

_____

6. Terence came to Canada shopping on a long weekend.
The exchange rate for his US money was $1.00 US to $1.25 Canadian.

a) How many Canadian dollars would Terence get for $500.00 US?

_____

b) Terence spent $504.90 Canadian altogether during his three days of stay in Canada.
What was his average spending per day?

_____

c) A jacket he purchased cost $39.95 Canadian.
What is this value in US dollars?

_____

In Your Words

Here are some of the important mathematical words of this unit.
Build your own glossary by recording definitions and examples here. The first one is done for you.

ratio _a comparison between_

two quantities measured in the same unit

$$\bigcirc\ \bigcirc\ \bigcirc\ \square\ \square$$

For example, the number of circles to the

number of squares is 3 to 2.

The ratio is 3:2.

terms of a ratio _____

_____

_____

_____

_____

_____

equivalent ratios _____

_____

_____

_____

_____

_____

simplest form _____

_____

_____

_____

_____

_____

rate _____

_____

_____

_____

_____

_____

unit rate _____

_____

_____

_____

_____

_____

List other mathematical words you need to know.

_____

Unit Review

2.1   **1.** Write each ratio.

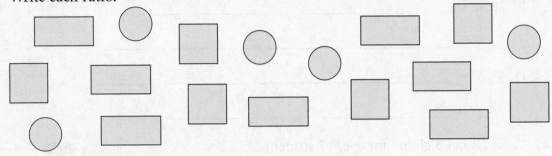

    a) squares to circles _____

    b) rectangles and circles to squares _____

    c) circles to total figures _____

2.2   **2. a)** Write three ratios equivalent to 2:5. Show your work.

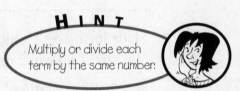

H I N T

Multiply or divide each
term by the same number.

    $2:5 = (2 \times \underline{\hspace{1cm}}):(5 \times \underline{\hspace{1cm}})$ $2:5 = \underline{\hspace{2cm}}$ $2:5 = \underline{\hspace{2cm}}$

        $= \underline{\hspace{1cm}} : \underline{\hspace{1cm}}$ $= \underline{\hspace{2cm}}$ $= \underline{\hspace{2cm}}$

    b) Write three ratios equivalent to 36:18. Show your work.

        $36:18 = \underline{\hspace{6cm}}$

                 $\underline{\hspace{6cm}}$

        $36:18 = \underline{\hspace{6cm}}$

                 $\underline{\hspace{6cm}}$

        $36:18 = \underline{\hspace{6cm}}$

                 $\underline{\hspace{6cm}}$

3. Write each ratio in simplest form.

a) $25:15 = (25 \div \underline{\hspace{1cm}}):(15 \div \underline{\hspace{1cm}})$

$= \underline{\hspace{1cm}} : \underline{\hspace{1cm}}$

b) $28:35 = $ _____

$= $ _____

c) $45:72 = $ _____

$= $ _____

2.3 **4.** Class 7B has 3 globes for every 7 students.
Class 7D has 2 globes for every 5 students.
Each class has the same number of students.
Which class has more globes? Explain.

Tip

Write each ratio with the same second term.

_____

_____

2.4 **5.** Madeline makes a scale drawing of the tennis court.
She used a scale of 2 cm to represent 1.5 m.

a) What is the ratio of a length in the drawing to the actual length?

_____

Tip

When you write a ratio of measurements, the units must be the same. Multiply to change metres to centimetres.

b) The length of the tennis court in the drawing is 40 cm.
What is the actual length of the tennis court?

_____

_____

2.5 **6.** Express as a unit rate.

a) The van travels 280 km in 4 h.

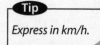

Tip

Express in km/h.

_____

b) Mikki jogs 2 km in 20 min.

_____

Geometry and Measurement

Just for Fun

Polygons

Unscramble the letters in each row to form the name of a polygon.

TARCNEEGL _____

IRCCEL _____

OHXNEGA _____

TOPNEGNA _____

ARUSEQ _____

GOONTAC _____

GTANIREL _____

EHGANTPO _____

Prism Search

How many ways can you find the word

PRISM in the diagram below? _____

```
      M   M   M   M   M
        S   S   S   S
          I   I   I
            R   R
              P
            R   R
          I   I   I
        S   S   S   S
      M   M   M   M   M
```

Sum or Product?

A Game for **2 to 4**

You need two number cubes, pencils, and paper.

Players take turns. On each turn, roll both number cubes.

If the sum of the two numbers is greater than the product of the two numbers, the player scores 3 points.
If the product of the two numbers is greater than the sum of the two numbers, the player scores 1 point.
If the sum and product are the same, the player scores no point.

Each player has 10 turns.
The player with the most points at the end of 10 turns is the winner.

Skills You'll Need

Identifying Polyhedra

A **polyhedron** is a solid with faces that are polygons.
Two faces meet at an edge.
Three or more edges meet at a vertex.
The **base** of a polyhedron is the face from which
the height is measured.

A **prism** has 2 congruent bases.
Its other faces are rectangles.
It is named for its bases.

A **pyramid** has 1 base.
Its other faces are triangles.
It is named for its base.

All the faces of a **regular polyhedron** are congruent.
The same number of faces and edges meet at each vertex.

Example 1

Identify each polyhedron as a prism or a pyramid.

a)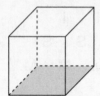

b)

Solution

a) The cube has 2 congruent square bases. Its other faces are squares.
   So, it is a rectangular prism.
   All of the faces are congruent, so a cube is a regular rectangular prism.

b) The polyhedron has 1 pentagonal base. Its other faces are triangles.
   So, it is a pentagonal pyramid.

✓ Check

1. Match each polyhedron with its name.

44   square
pyramid

tetrahedron

octagonal
prism

triangular
prism

hexagonal
pyramid

Using Isometric Dot Paper to Draw a Cube

You can use your skill of drawing a cube to draw other figures on isometric dot paper.

Example 2

Draw this rectangular prism
on isometric dot paper.

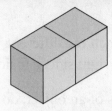

i) Join 2 dots for
one vertical edge.

ii) Join pairs of dots diagonally for the
front horizontal edges, top, and bottom.

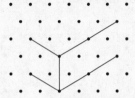

iii) Join the dots for the other
vertical edges.

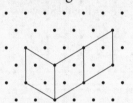

iv) Join dots diagonally for the back
horizontal edges at the top.

Shade visible faces
to get a 3-D look.

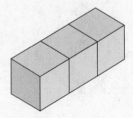

✓ **Check**

2. Complete the drawing of each
object on isometric dot paper.

a)

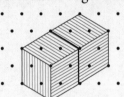

b)

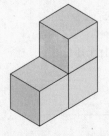

H I N T

You can first draw one cube with all
three faces showing. Then add the
faces of the adjacent cubes.

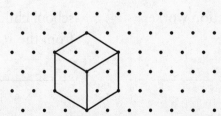

Quick Review

➤ You can use square dot paper to sketch the different views of an object.
The different views are: front, back, right side, left side, and top.

➤ When you sketch the different views of an object, do not include details
such as holes or other markings on the faces.

Here are the different views of an object.

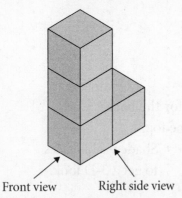

Front view   Right side view

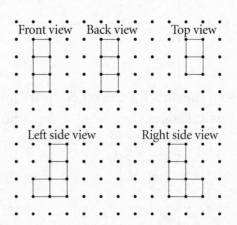

Practice

1. Many signs are views of objects.
Identify the view (front, back, side, or top) of the object on each sign.

a)

construction worker
from the

_____

b)

school children
from the

_____

c)

road from the

_____

2. Each object is made using linking cubes.
Draw the back, side, and top views of each object.
The front view is drawn for you.

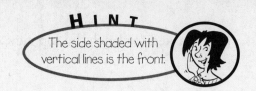
HINT
The side shaded with vertical lines is the front.

a)

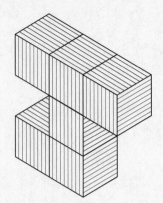

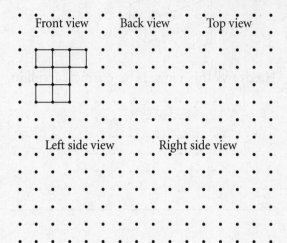

Front view   Back view   Top view

Left side view   Right side view

b)

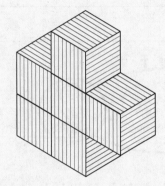

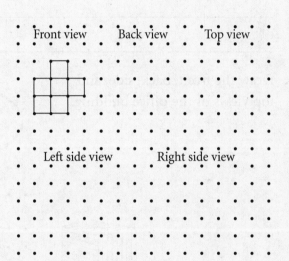

Front view   Back view   Top view

Left side view   Right side view

3. Match each object in the top row with its front view in the bottom row.

Key to Success

If certain manipulatives, such as linking cubes or building blocks, are not available, think of something you have in your home. For example, you can use sugar cubes or number cubes to model solids made from linking cubes.

47

4. Joey is asked to sketch the top view of this object.

He draws this view. Is he correct? Explain.

Top view

_____

_____

_____

5. Draw the front, back, side, and top views of the office building.

H I N T

Ask, "How many levels would I see on the left side of the building?"

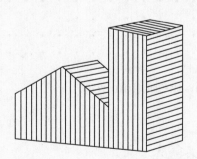

Quick Review

➤ You can show a 3-dimensional object in 2 dimensions
using isometric dot paper.
Draw parallel edges on an object as parallel line segments.

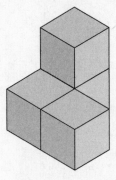

H I N T

Isometric means "equal measure". On
isometric dot paper, all adjacent dots
are an equal distance from each other.

First, draw all vertical
edges.

Next, draw all horizontal
edges that appear to slant
down to the right.

Then, draw all horizontal
edges that appear to slant
up to the right.
Shade the faces for a
3-D effect.

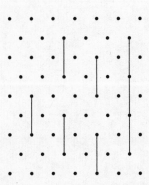

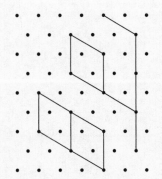

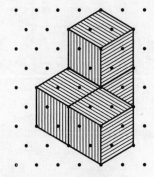

➤ A **pictorial diagram** shows the shape of an object in 2 dimensions.
It gives the impression of 3 dimensions because
the diagram is sketched using translations.

To sketch a cube:
Draw a square.

Draw another square that
is an image of the first
square after a translation
up and to the right.

Connect corresponding
vertices for a sketch
of a cube.

1. Each object is made using linking cubes.
Complete the drawing of each object.

a)

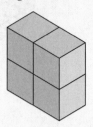

b)

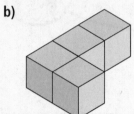

2. Draw a pictorial diagram of each object.

a)

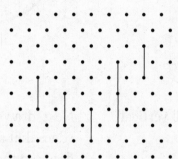

b)

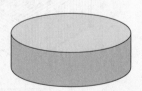

3. An object is made using 4 linking cubes.
The top, front, and right side views of the object are shown.
Sketch a 3-D picture of the object.

Top view   Front view   Right side view

4. One possible arrangement of 3 cubes is shown.
Sketch 2 other objects that you can make with 3 cubes
on plain paper and then on isometric dot paper.

H I N T

First draw one cube
with all faces showing.
Then add the faces of
the adjacent cubes.

5. Find an object in the shape of a rectangular prism in your home.
Find a cylindrical object in your home or school.
Name each object and sketch a 3-D picture of it.

Which object did you find easier to sketch? Why?

_____

_____

Quick Review

➤ A net is a pattern that you can cut out, fold, and tape to make a polyhedron.

➤ A regular polyhedron has congruent faces.
A regular octahedron has 8 congruent faces. Each face is an equilateral triangle.

➤ When you have made a polyhedron, you can look at it to find out more about its properties.
Look at the net and the polyhedron that is folded from the net.

Net

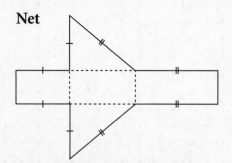

Polyhedron

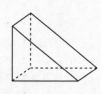

The polyhedron has 2 congruent triangular bases.
Its other faces are rectangles.
So, the polyhedron is a triangular prism.

Practice

1. Look at the net and the polyhedron that is folded from the net.

Net

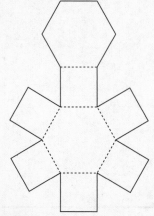

Polyhedron

a) How many faces does the polyhedron have? _____

b) How many edges does it have? _____

c) How many vertices does it have? _____

d) How many congruent faces?

_____ hexagons, _____ rectangles

e) The polyhedron is a _____.

2. Look at each net and the polyhedron that was folded from the net.

a) Net   **Polyhedron**

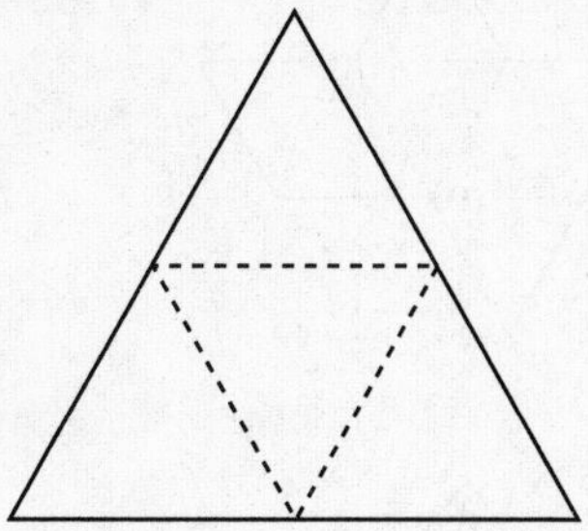

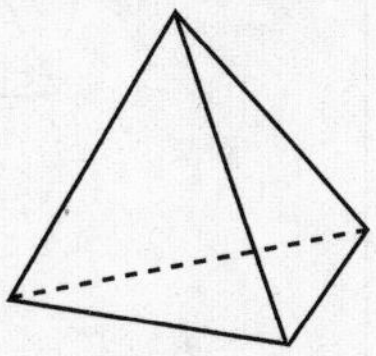

The polyhedron is a

_____

b) Net   **Polyhedron**

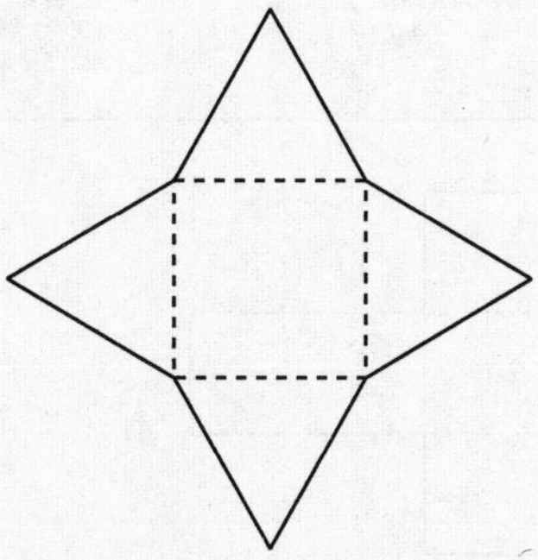

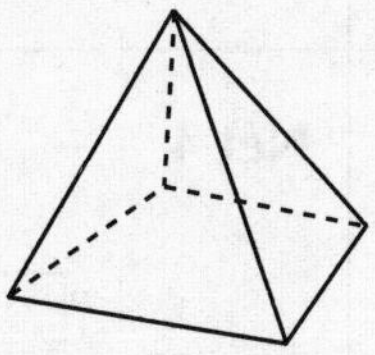

The polyhedron is a

_____

HINT

To compare polyhedra, compare: number of faces, edges, and vertices; shapes of faces; shapes of bases.

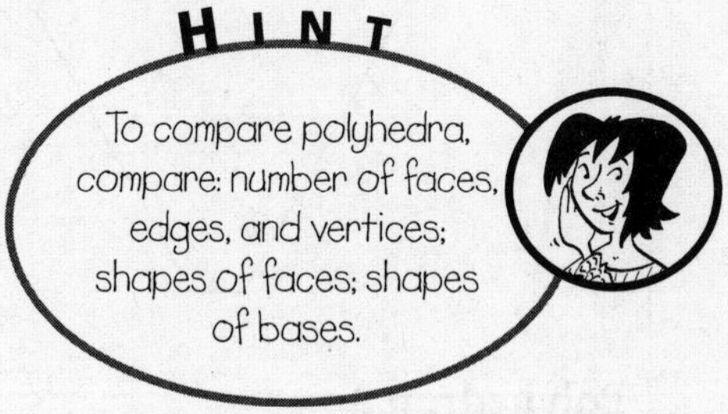

c) How are the polyhedra in parts a and b the same? How are they different?

_____

_____

_____

_____

3. Suppose you folded this net into a polyhedron. Describe the polyhedron you would create.

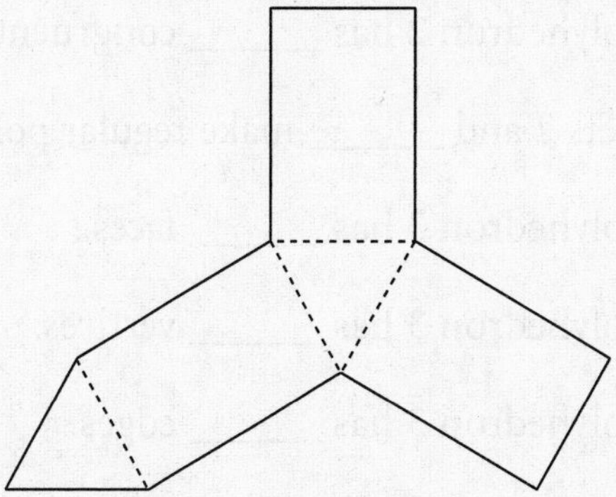

_____

_____

4. Look at the nets and the polyhedra that are folded from the nets.
Complete the descriptions for the polyhedra.

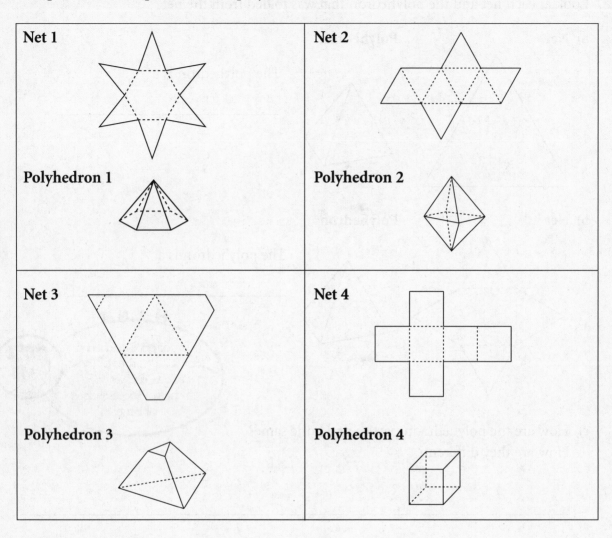

a) Polyhedron 1 has _____ faces.

b) Polyhedron 1 has _____ edges.

c) Polyhedron 1 has _____ hexagonal face.

d) Polyhedron 2 has _____ congruent faces

e) Nets 2 and _____ make regular polyhedra.

f) Polyhedron 3 has _____ faces.

g) Polyhedron 3 has _____ vertices.

h) Polyhedron 3 has _____ edges.

i) Polyhedron 3 has _____ triangular faces.

j) Polyhedron 4 has _____ pairs of parallel faces.

Quick Review

➤ The letters that you use to represent unknown dimensions of a figure are **variables**.

For a rectangle:
Use b to represent the length of the base.
Use h to represent the height.

For a square:
Use s to represent the side length.

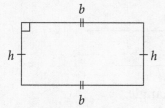 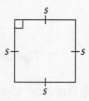

Area $A = bh$
Perimeter $P = 2(b + h)$

Area $A = s \times s$
or $A = s^2$
Perimeter $P = 4s$

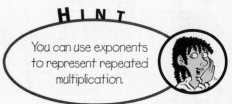

HINT
You can use exponents to represent repeated multiplication.

➤ When you know the dimensions of a figure, you can **substitute** for the variables in a formula with numbers.

A rectangle has base 7 cm and height 4 cm.
Find its area and perimeter.

7 cm

4 cm

Area, $A = bh$
Substitute: $b = 7$ and $h = 4$
$A = 7 \times 4$
$A = 28$
The area is 28 cm².

Perimeter, $P = 2(b + h)$
Substitute: $b = 7$ and $h = 4$
$P = 2(7 + 4)$
$P = 2(11)$
$P = 22$
The perimeter is 22 cm.

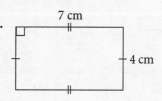

HINT
Use order of operations. Do the operation in brackets first. Then multiply.

1. Use the formula: $A = bh$ Find the area of each rectangle.

a)

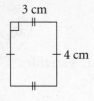

3 cm

4 cm

$A = bh$

Substitute: $b = 3$ and $h =$ _____

$A =$ _____ × _____

  = _____

The area is _____ .

b)

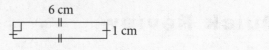

6 cm

1 cm

$A = bh$

Substitute: $b =$ _____ and $h =$ _____

_____

_____

The area is _____ .

2. Use the formula: $P = 2(b + h)$ Find the perimeter of each rectangle.

a)

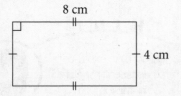

8 cm

4 cm

$P = 2(b + h)$

Substitute: $b = 8$ and $h =$ _____

$P = 2(8 +$ _____ $)$

  $= 2($ _____ $)$

  $=$ _____

The perimeter is _____ .

b)

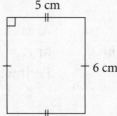

5 cm

6 cm

$P = 2(b + h)$

Substitute: $b =$ _____ and $h =$ _____

$P =$ _____

  $=$ _____

  $=$ _____

The perimeter is _____ .

3. Use the formulas: $P = 4s$ and $A = s^2$ Find the perimeter and area of the square.

$P = 4s$

Substitute: $s = 4$

$P = 4 \times$ _____

  $=$ _____

The perimeter is _____ cm.

$A = s^2$

Substitute: $s = 4$

$A =$ _____

  $=$ _____

The area is _____ cm^2.

4 cm

4. Find the perimeter and area of each figure.

a)

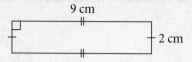

Area = _____

Perimeter = _____

b)

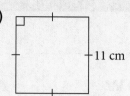

Area = _____

Perimeter = _____

c)

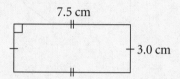

Area = _____

Perimeter = _____

d)

Area = _____

Perimeter = _____

5. A rectangle is formed by 4 squares as shown.
Find the area and perimeter of the rectangle.
Show your work.

The area of the rectangle is _____.   The perimeter is _____.

Quick Review

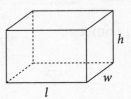

➤ The **surface area** of a rectangular prism is the sum of the areas of its rectangular faces. The surface area is the same as the area of the prism's net.

➤ The formula for the surface area of a rectangular prism is:
$SA = 2lh + 2lw + 2hw$
where l represents the length of the prism,
  h represents the height of the prism, and
  w represents the width of the prism.

➤ To find the surface area of a given rectangular prism, substitute the actual measures for the variables in the formula.

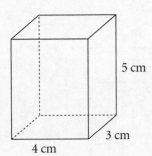

$SA = 2lh + 2lw + 2hw$
Substitute: $l = 4$, $h = 5$, and $w = 3$
$SA = 2(4 \times 5) + 2(4 \times 3) + 2(5 \times 3)$
  $= 2(20) + 2(12) + 2(15)$
  $= 40 + 24 + 30$
  $= 94$
The surface area of the rectangular prism is 94 cm².

Practice

1. Find the surface area of the rectangular prism.

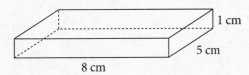

$SA = 2lh + 2lw + 2hw$

Substitute: $l = 8$, $h = $ _____, and $w = $ _____

$SA = 2(8 \times$ _____$) + 2(8 \times$ _____$) + 2($ _____ $\times$ _____$)$

  $= 2($ _____$) + 2($ _____$) + 2($ _____$)$

  $= $ _____ $+$ _____ $+$ _____

  $= $ _____

HINT
Use order of operations. Do the operation in brackets first. Then multiply. Then add.

The surface area is _____.

2. Glenda and Louis each designs a rectangular package.
Whose package has the greater surface area? Show your work.

Glenda's package:

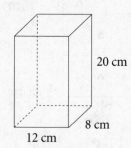

20 cm

8 cm

12 cm

$SA = 2lh + 2lw + 2hw$

$SA = $ _____ + _____ + _____

= _____

= _____

_____

Louis's package:

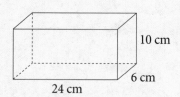

10 cm

6 cm

24 cm

$SA = 2lh + 2lw + 2hw$

$SA = $ _____ + _____ + _____

= _____

= _____

_____

_____ > _____ So, _____ package has the greater surface area.

3. The object has the shape of a rectangular prism, but part of a face is missing.
Find the surface area of the object and show your work.

a)

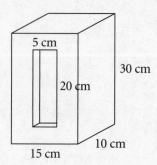

5 cm

30 cm

20 cm

15 cm

10 cm

Find the surface area of the complete prism.

_____

_____

_____

_____

The missing area is in the shape of a rectangle.
Use the formula: $A = bh$
Substitute: $b = 5$ and $h = 20$

Missing area = _____ × _____ = _____

Surface area = surface area of complete prism − missing area

= _____ − _____

= _____

The surface area of the object is _____.

4. Hannah's dresser is a shaped like a rectangular prism.
Hannah painted the top, front, and sides of her dresser brown.
What area did she paint?

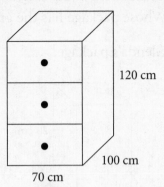

120 cm

100 cm

70 cm

Hannah painted an area of _____.

5. The rectangular prism B is made from 8
of the smaller rectangular prism A on its left.

A 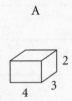 B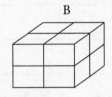

2

4   3

a) Find the surface of the each prism. Show your work.

b) What do you think happens to the surface area of a rectangular prism
when each length is doubled?

_____

_____

_____

60

Quick Review

➤ The formula for the volume V of a rectangular prism is: $V = lwh$
  where l represents the length of the prism,
          h represents the height of the prism, and
          w represents the width of the prism.

➤ Since lw is the area of the base, you can also write
  the volume of a rectangular prism as: $V = Ah$
  where A represents the area of the base and
          h represents the height of the prism.

You can find the volume of this rectangular prism in two ways.

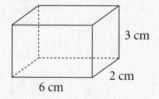

3 cm
2 cm
6 cm

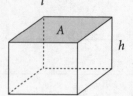

H I N T

The base of a rectangular prism can be any face of the prism.

One way:
Volume = length × width × height
$\quad V = lwh$
Substitute: $l = 6$, $w = 2$, and $h = 3$
$\quad V = 6 \times 2 \times 3$
$\quad\quad = 12 \times 3$
$\quad\quad = 36$

Another way:
Volume = base area × height
$\quad V = Ah$
Substitute $l = 6$ and $w = 2$ into $A = lw$
$\quad A = 6 \times 2$
$\quad\quad = 12$
Substitute: $A = 12$ and $h = 3$
$\quad V = 12 \times 3$
$\quad\quad = 36$

The volume is the same either way.
The volume of the rectangular prism is 36 cm³.

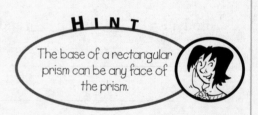

Practice

1. a) Use the formula: $V = lwh$

Find the volume of each rectangular prism in the robot.

Head: $l =$ _____, $w =$ _____, and $h =$ _____

$V =$ _____

  $=$ _____

The volume of the head is _____.

Neck: $l =$ _____, $w =$ _____, and $h =$ _____

$V =$ _____

  $=$ _____

The volume of the neck is _____.

Body: $l =$ _____, $w =$ _____, and $h =$ _____

$V =$ _____

  $=$ _____

The volume of the body is _____.

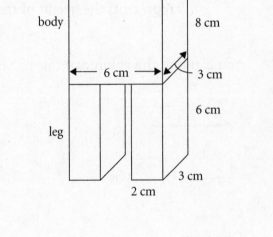

One arm: _____   One leg: _____

$V =$ _____ $V =$ _____

  $=$ _____ $=$ _____

The volume of one arm is _____.   The volume of one leg is _____.

b) Find the total volume of the rectangular prisms in the robot.

Total volume = _____

             $=$ _____

The total volume of the robot is _____.

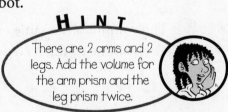

HINT

There are 2 arms and 2 legs. Add the volume for the arm prism and the leg prism twice.

2. Find the volume of each rectangular prism.

a)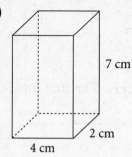

$V = lwh$

Substitute: $l = $ _____, $w = 2$, and $h = 7$

$V = $ _____

$= $ _____

The volume of the rectangular prism is _____ cm³.

b)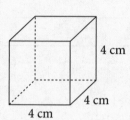

$V = lwh$

Substitute: $l = $ _____, $w = $ _____, and $h = $ _____

$V = $ _____

$= $ _____

The volume of the rectangular prism is _____.

Write a formula for the volume of a cube that has side length l: _____.

3. Find the volume of this rectangular prism. Show your work.

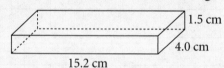

> **Tip**
>
> *Use a calculator when it helps.*

The volume of the rectangular prism is _____.

4. Complete the sentences about rectangular prism A.

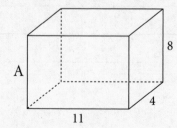

• Volume of A: _____

• Volume of A when its width is doubled: _____

• Volume of A when its length and width are both doubled: _____

• Volume of A when its length, width, and height are all halved: _____

In Your Words

Here are some of the important mathematical words of this unit.
Build your own glossary by recording definitions and examples here. The first one is done for you.

prism *a solid with*
2 congruent faces as bases and
other faces that are rectangles
For example, this is a triangular prism.

pyramid _____

surface area _____

polyhedron _____

volume _____

isometric drawing _____

List other mathematical words you need to know.

_____

Unit Review

LESSON

3.1 **1.** Draw the front, back, side, and top views of this object.

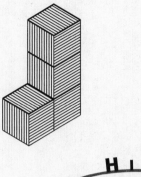

H I N T

The side shaded with horizontal lines is the right side.

3.2 **2.** Complete the drawing of the object.

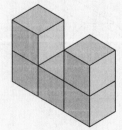

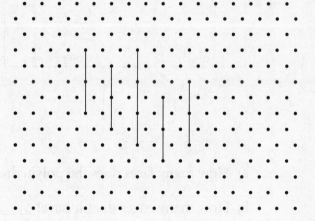

3. Draw a pictorial diagram of each object.

a)

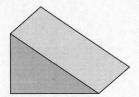

b)

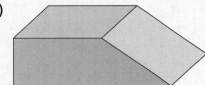

3.3 **4.** Look at the net and the polyhedron that is folded from the net.

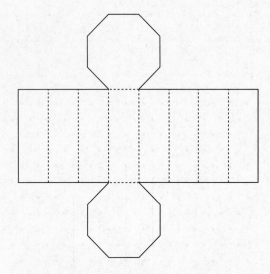

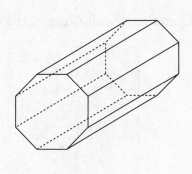

a) How many faces does the polyhedron have? _____

b) How many edges does it have? _____

c) How many vertices does it have? _____

d) How many congruent faces are there?

_____ congruent octagons, _____ congruent rectangles

e) The polyhedron is an _____.

5. Rashid's backyard is a rectangle that measures 15 m by 8 m.
Allie's backyard is a square that measures 11 m by 11 m.

a) Find the perimeter of each backyard.

Rashid's backyard: $P = 2(b + h)$

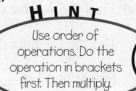

HINT

Use order of operations. Do the operation in brackets first. Then multiply.

Substitute: _____

_____

_____

_____

_____

Allie's backyard: $P = 4s$

Substitute: _____

_____

_____

_____

b) Find the area of each backyard. Whose backyard has the greater area?

Rashid's backyard: $A = bh$

Substitute: _____

_____

_____

_____

Allie's backyard: $A = s^2$

Substitute: _____

_____

_____

_____

_____ m² > _____ m² So, _____ backyard has the greater area.

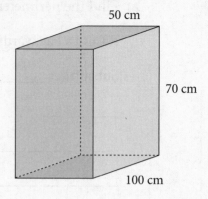

6. Chen builds a doghouse for his puppy.

a) Find the volume of the doghouse.

Use the formula: $V = lwh$

Substitute: $l =$ _____, $w =$ _____, and $h =$ _____

$V =$ _____

$ =$ _____

The volume of the doghouse is _____.

b) Find the total surface area of the doghouse.
The dog house is a rectangular prism.

Use the formula: $SA = 2lh + 2lw + 2hw$

Substitute: _____

$SA =$ _____

$ =$ _____

$ =$ _____

The surface area of the doghouse is _____.

c) Chen cuts a doorway in the doghouse, so the puppy
can get into it. Find the new surface area of the doghouse.

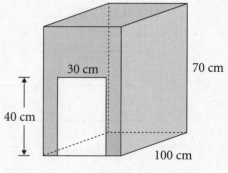

The doorway is a rectangle.
Use the formula: $A = bh$

Substitute: _____

$A =$ _____

$ =$ _____

The area of the doorway is _____.

New surface area = surface area of doghouse – area of doorway

$ =$ _____

$ =$ _____

The new surface area of the doghouse is _____.

Fractions and Decimals

Just for Fun

Hidden Message

Find the message hidden in each box. The first one is done for you.

(**done4U**)　　　(**mill1ion**)　　　(**lem**
π)

done for you　　　_____　　　_____

What Tree Is It?

What tree does a math teacher climb?

_____ _____ _____ _____ _____ _____ _____ _____

To solve the riddle:

- unscramble the letters in each row to form a math word
- for each word, circle the letter indicated in brackets

The circled letters will solve the riddle.

gaptinree	___ ___ ___ ___ ___ ___ ___ ___ ___	(last letter)
tvaeilnuqe	___ ___ ___ ___ ___ ___ ___ ___ ___ ___	(1st letter)
mnoocm	___ ___ ___ ___ ___ ___	(2nd letter)
ledcima	___ ___ ___ ___ ___ ___ ___	(5th letter)
rotaremun	___ ___ ___ ___ ___ ___ ___ ___ ___	(4th letter)
ncafrtio	___ ___ ___ ___ ___ ___ ___ ___	(5th letter)
dnmortaeino	___ ___ ___ ___ ___ ___ ___ ___ ___ ___ ___	(last letter)
umltipyl	___ ___ ___ ___ ___ ___ ___ ___	(last letter)

Skills You'll Need

Adding and Subtracting Fractions with Pattern Blocks

You can use Pattern Blocks to model adding and subtracting fractions.

Fraction represented: 1 $\frac{1}{2}$ $\frac{1}{3}$ $\frac{1}{6}$

Example 1

Use Pattern Blocks to add and subtract.

a) $\frac{1}{6} + \frac{1}{3}$

b) $\frac{2}{3} - \frac{1}{2}$

Solution

a) $\frac{1}{6} + \frac{1}{3}$

b) $\frac{2}{3} - \frac{1}{2}$

$\frac{1}{6}$ $\frac{1}{3}$ $\frac{1}{2}$

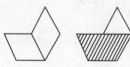

Show $\frac{2}{3}$ Cover $\frac{1}{2}$

$\frac{2}{3} - \frac{1}{2} = \frac{1}{6}$ $\frac{1}{6}$ is not covered.

✔ Check

1. Use Pattern Blocks to add. Sketch the Pattern Blocks and answer.

a) $\frac{2}{3} + \frac{1}{3}$

b) $\frac{1}{6} + \frac{1}{6}$

2. Use Pattern Blocks to subtract. Sketch the Pattern Blocks and answer.

a) $\frac{5}{6} - \frac{1}{2}$

b) $1 - \frac{2}{3}$

Multiplying by 0.1, 0.01, and 0.001

To multiply a number by 0.1, 0.01, or 0.001, shift the decimal point in the number.
To multiply by 0.1, move the decimal point 1 place to the left.
To multiply by 0.01, move the decimal point 2 places to the left.
To multiply by 0.001, move the decimal point 3 places to the left.

Example 2

Multiply.
a) 152×0.1 b) 280×0.01 c) 39×0.01

Solution

a) $152 \times 0.1 = 15.2$ Move the decimal point 1 place to the left.

b) $280 \times 0.01 = 2.80$ Move the decimal point 2 places to the left.

c) $39 \times 0.01 = 0.039$ Move the decimal point 3 places to the left.

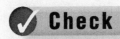
Check

3. Multiply.

   a) 7×0.1 b) 42×0.1 c) 600×0.1

   _____   _____   _____

   d) 2783×0.01 e) 22×0.01 f) 9×0.01

   _____   _____   _____

   g) 275×0.001 h) 21×0.001 i) 4×0.001

   _____   _____   _____

4. To convert from centimetres to metres, multiply the length in centimetres by 0.01.
   Convert these measurements to metres.
   Show your work.

   a) 32 cm   b) 12.1 cm   c) 7.9 cm

   _____   _____   _____

   _____   _____   _____

Operations with Decimals

Example 3

Evaluate.

a) 56.3 + 5.32   b) 64.3 − 55.9   c) 523.8 × 3   d) 6.23 ÷ 2

Solution

a) 56.3 + 5.32
   Line up the decimal points.
   Add the digits as you do with adding whole numbers.
   Place the decimal point in the answer.

Estimate: 55 + 5 = 60

$$\begin{array}{r} 56.3 \\ + \ 5.32 \\ \hline 61.62 \end{array}$$

b) 64.3 − 55.9
   Line up the decimal points.
   Subtract the digits as you do with subtracting whole numbers.
   Place the decimal point in the answer.

Estimate: 65 − 55 = 10

$$\begin{array}{r} 64.3 \\ - \ 55.9 \\ \hline 8.4 \end{array}$$

c) 523.8 × 3
   As with whole numbers, multiply: 5238 × 3
   Place the decimal point in the answer using the estimate.
   So, 523.8 × 3 = 1571.4

Estimate: 500 × 3 = 1500

$$\begin{array}{r} 5238 \\ \times \quad 3 \\ \hline 15714 \end{array}$$

d) 6.23 ÷ 2
   As with whole numbers, divide: 623 ÷ 2
   Place the decimal point in the answer using the estimate.
   So, 6.23 ÷ 2 = 3.115

Estimate: 6 ÷ 2 = 3

$$2 \overline{)\ 623^10}$$
$$311\ 5$$

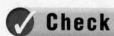

Check

5. Evaluate.

a) 13.1 + 2.4   b) 87.6 − 73.5   c) 32.5 × 2   d) 18.4 ÷ 4

e) 37.25 + 41.2   f) 23.12 − 12.6   g) 26.7 × 3   h) 47.8 ÷ 5

> **Tip**
> Rewrite the question to make calculation easier.

Comparing and Ordering Decimals

There are two ways you can compare decimals.

To compare 2.42 and 2.35, you can either

• mark each decimal on a number line that shows tenths.

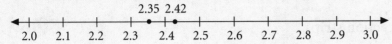

2.42 is between 2.4 and 2.5 and 2.35 is between 2.3 and 2.4.

So, 2.42 > 2.35

or

• compare digits beginning from the highest place value.
  In the ones place, 2.42 and 2.35 have the same value, which is 2.
  In the tenths place, 4 is greater than 3.
  So, 2.42 > 2.35

Example 4

Order the decimals from least to greatest.
8.92, 2.52, 9.83, 0.05

Solution

Mark the decimals on a number line.

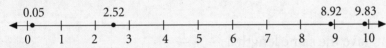

The decimals from least to greatest: 0.05, 2.52, 8.92, 9.83

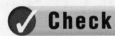 **Check**

6. Use a number line to order the decimals in each set from least to greatest.

   a) 4.21, 4.11, 4.82, 5.01   b) 8.23, 8.45, 6.23, 7.34

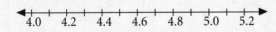

   c) 3.07, 3.04, 3.21, 3.14   d) 5.1, 5.01, 4.89, 4.98

Quick Review

You can model fractions with **fraction strips**.

To add $\frac{1}{6} + \frac{1}{3}$, estimate first.

Think: $\frac{1}{6} < \frac{1}{3}$; $\frac{1}{3} + \frac{1}{3} < 1$ So, $\frac{1}{6} + \frac{1}{3} < 1$

Model $\frac{1}{6}$ and $\frac{1}{3}$ with fraction strips.

Align the 2 fraction strips.
Find a single strip that has the same length.

There are 2 strips, $\frac{3}{6}$ and $\frac{1}{2}$, that have the same length as $\frac{1}{6} + \frac{1}{3}$.

$\frac{3}{6}$ and $\frac{1}{2}$ are **equivalent fractions**.

They represent the same amount.

Practice

1. Use fraction strips to add. $\frac{3}{8} + \frac{1}{4}$

$\frac{3}{8} + \frac{1}{4} = $ _____

HINT

Find an equivalent fraction for $\frac{1}{4}$.

KEY TO SUCCESS

Form a contact circle with 2 classmates in case you miss information from class while you are absent.

2. Use fraction strips to add. $\frac{1}{2} + \frac{1}{5}$

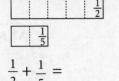

$\frac{1}{2} + \frac{1}{5} =$ _____

3. Add. Estimate first.

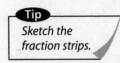

Tip

Sketch the fraction strips.

a) $\frac{1}{10} + \frac{1}{5} =$ _____

b) $\frac{1}{6} + \frac{1}{2} =$ _____

4. Add. Estimate first.

a) $\frac{2}{3} + \frac{2}{6} =$ _____

b) $\frac{2}{5} + \frac{3}{10} =$ _____

5. The girls' baseball team shared a large chocolate bar.
Kenika ate $\frac{1}{3}$ of the chocolate bar, Charlene ate $\frac{1}{3}$, and Krithika ate $\frac{1}{9}$.

a) What fraction of the chocolate bar did Kenika and Charlene eat?

_____

b) What fraction of the chocolate bar did the 3 girls eat?

_____

c) What fraction of the chocolate bar was left? Explain.

_____

_____

Quick Review

There are many models that help you add fractions.

Circle models are useful when the sum of the fractions is less than 1.

Use fraction strips and a number line when the sum of the fractions is greater than 1.

To add $\frac{2}{3} + \frac{1}{2}$, estimate first.

Think: $\frac{2}{3} > \frac{1}{2}$ So, $\frac{2}{3} + \frac{1}{2} > 1$

Model each fraction with a fraction strip.

Place the fraction strips end-to-end on a number line that shows halves.

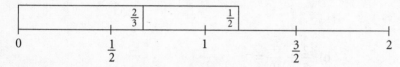

The right end of the strips does not line up with a fraction.

Try using a number line that shows thirds.

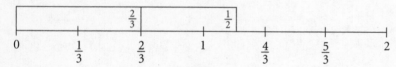

The right end of the strips still does not line up with a fraction.

Find a number line that shows sixths.

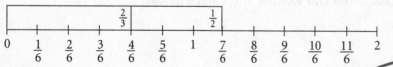

The right end of the strips lines up with $\frac{7}{6}$.

So, $\frac{2}{3} + \frac{1}{2} = \frac{7}{6}$

HINT

The lowest common multiple of the denominators 3 and 2 is 6.

Practice

1. Add. Use fraction strips and this number line to help.

```
├─┼─┼─┼─┼─┼─┼─┼─┼─┼─┼─┼─┼─┼─┼─┼─┼─┼─┼─┤
0  1   2   3   4   5   6   7   8   9  1  11  12  13  14  15  16  17  18  19  2
  ──  ──  ──  ──  ──  ──  ──  ──  ──    ──  ──  ──  ──  ──  ──  ──  ──  ──
  10  10  10  10  10  10  10  10  10    10  10  10  10  10  10  10  10  10
```

$\frac{3}{5} + \frac{3}{10} = \underline{\hspace{1cm}}$

2. Use fraction strips and these number lines to help you add fractions. Estimate first.

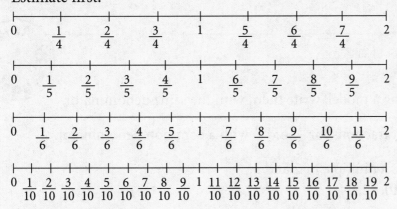

a) $\frac{1}{2} + \frac{1}{4}$ Estimate:

$\frac{1}{2} + \frac{1}{4}$ _____ 1

$\frac{1}{2} + \frac{1}{4} =$ _____

b) $\frac{6}{6} + \frac{3}{4}$ Estimate:

$\frac{6}{6} + \frac{3}{4}$ _____ 1

$\frac{6}{6} + \frac{3}{4} =$ _____

c) $\frac{9}{10} + \frac{3}{5}$ Estimate:

$\frac{9}{10} + \frac{3}{5}$ _____ 1

$\frac{9}{10} + \frac{3}{5} =$ _____

3. Add. Use models to help.

a) $\frac{2}{2} + \frac{1}{5} =$ _____

b) $\frac{3}{6} + \frac{2}{3} =$ _____

4. Find as many pairs of fractions as you can that have a sum of 1. Write 4 pairs of them in the blanks provided.

Tip
Model fractions with fraction strips and place them on a number line to check.

_____   _____

_____   _____

H I N T
You can use circle models.

5. Robert and his brother ordered a pizza. Robert ate $\frac{1}{4}$ of the pizza.

His brother ate $\frac{3}{8}$ of the pizza.

How much pizza was left?

_____

Quick Review

To add fractions without using a model, write them with the same denominator.

To add $\frac{1}{2} + \frac{3}{5}$, find equivalent fractions for $\frac{1}{2}$ and $\frac{3}{5}$ with a common denominator.

The common denominator is a multiple of 2 and 5.
Multiples of 2 are: 2, 4, 6, 8, **10**, 12, 14, . . .
Multiples of 5 are: 5, **10**, 15, . . .
10 is a common multiple of 2 and 5.
So, you can use 10 as the common denominator.

Then, write the equivalent fractions for $\frac{1}{2}$ and $\frac{3}{5}$ with 10 as denominator.

To get equivalent fractions, multiply the numerator and denominator by the same number.

$$\frac{1}{2} = \frac{1 \times 5}{2 \times 5} = \frac{5}{10} \qquad\qquad \frac{3}{5} = \frac{3 \times 2}{5 \times 2} = \frac{6}{10}$$

$$\frac{1}{2} + \frac{3}{5} = \frac{5}{10} + \frac{6}{10} = \frac{11}{10}$$

Tip
Use fraction strips to check equivalent fractions.

You can write a fraction greater than 1 as a mixed number.

$$\frac{11}{10} = 1\frac{1}{10}$$

You can also divide to get equivalent fractions. The equivalent fraction is in **simplest form** when you divide by the GCF of the numerator and denominator.

$$\frac{6}{10} = \frac{6 \div 2}{10 \div 2} = \frac{3}{5}$$

Practice

1. Write 2 equivalent fractions for each.

   a) $\frac{3}{5}$ $\frac{3}{5} = \frac{3 \times 2}{5 \times 2} = $ _____

        $\frac{3}{5} = \dfrac{3 \times \rule{1cm}{0.4pt}}{5 \times \rule{1cm}{0.4pt}} = $ _____

   b) $\frac{4}{6}$ $\frac{4}{6} = \dfrac{4 \div \rule{1cm}{0.4pt}}{6 \div \rule{1cm}{0.4pt}} = $ _____

        $\frac{4}{6} = \dfrac{4 \times \rule{1cm}{0.4pt}}{6 \times \rule{1cm}{0.4pt}} = $ _____

2. Add.

a) $\frac{2}{9} + \frac{1}{3}$

The multiples of 9 are: _____

The multiples of 3 are: _____

The lowest common multiple of 9 and 3 is _____.

Use this as a common denominator.

$$\frac{2}{9} + \frac{1}{3} = \frac{2 \times \rule{2cm}{0.4pt}}{9 \times \rule{1cm}{0.4pt}} + \frac{1 \times \rule{2cm}{0.4pt}}{3 \times \rule{1cm}{0.4pt}}$$

$$= \rule{8cm}{0.4pt}$$

$$= \rule{8cm}{0.4pt}$$

b) $\frac{7}{10} + \frac{1}{6}$

The lowest common multiple of 10 and 6 is _____.

$$\frac{7}{10} + \frac{1}{6} = \rule{8cm}{0.4pt}$$

$$= \rule{8cm}{0.4pt}$$

$$= \rule{8cm}{0.4pt}$$

3. Add.

a) $\frac{5}{6} + \frac{1}{3} = $ _____

b) $\frac{2}{3} + \frac{3}{4} = $ _____

c) $\frac{3}{8} + \frac{1}{2} + \frac{1}{4} = $ _____

Tip
You can write a fraction greater than 1 as a mixed number.

79

4. Add.

HINT

To add 2 mixed numbers:
- Add the whole numbers.
- Add the fractions.
- Write the sum as a mixed number.

a) $2\frac{1}{2} + 3\frac{2}{5}$

$2 + 3 =$ _____ $\frac{1}{2} + \frac{2}{5} =$ _____

So, $2\frac{1}{2} + 3\frac{2}{5} =$ _____

b) $7\frac{1}{9} + 3\frac{1}{6} =$ _____

5. Linda is making new curtains for her kitchen and living room windows.

She needs $1\frac{1}{3}$ m of fabric for the kitchen and $2\frac{3}{5}$ m for the living room.

How many metres of fabric does Linda need altogether?

_____

6. Three students shared a pizza.

Anna ate $\frac{1}{10}$, Edmond ate $\frac{3}{5}$, and Kevin ate $\frac{3}{10}$.

What fraction of the pizza was eaten by the 3 students? Show your work.

_____

How much pizza was left?

_____

Quick Review

When you subtract 7 − 3, you could think:
What do I add to 3 to make 7?
You can use the same strategy to subtract fractions.

To subtract $\frac{7}{8} - \frac{1}{4}$, use fraction strips and a number line.

The lowest common multiple of 8 and 4 is 8.
Use a number line that shows eighths.

Place the $\frac{1}{4}$ strip on the number line with its right end at $\frac{7}{8}$.

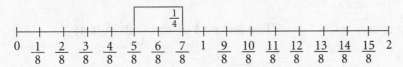

The left end of the strip is at $\frac{5}{8}$.

So, $\frac{7}{8} - \frac{1}{4} = \frac{5}{8}$

Practice

1. Subtract.

a) $\frac{6}{10} - \frac{2}{5}$

HINT

What do you add to $\frac{2}{5}$ to get $\frac{6}{10}$?

The lowest common multiple of 10 and 5 is _____.

Use a number line that shows _____.

Place the $\frac{2}{5}$ fraction strip on the number line with the right end at $\frac{6}{10}$.
The left end of the $\frac{2}{5}$ strip is at

_____.

So, $\frac{6}{10} - \frac{2}{5} =$ _____

b) $2 - \frac{2}{3}$

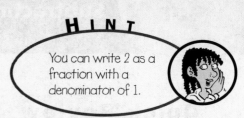

H I N T

You can write 2 as a fraction with a denominator of 1.

The left end of the $\frac{2}{3}$ strip is at _____. So, $2 - \frac{2}{3} =$ _____

2. Subtract.

a) $\frac{5}{6} - \frac{1}{6}$

Use a number line that shows

_____.

b) $\frac{7}{8} - \frac{3}{4}$

Use a number line that shows

_____.

The left end of the $\frac{1}{6}$ strip is at _____.

So, $\frac{5}{6} - \frac{1}{6} =$ _____

The left end of the $\frac{3}{4}$ strip is at _____.

So, $\frac{7}{8} - \frac{3}{4} =$ _____

3. Subtract.

a) $\frac{9}{10} - \frac{1}{2} =$ _____

b) $\frac{5}{6} - \frac{1}{2} =$ _____

c) $\frac{11}{6} - \frac{1}{3} =$ _____

d) $1 - \frac{5}{8} =$ _____

4. a) Write 5 subtractions with a difference of $\frac{1}{2}$.

_____ _____ _____ _____ _____

b) How are these subtractions the same?

_____

_____

Quick Review

To subtract fractions without using a model, write them with the same denominator.

To subtract $\frac{2}{3} - \frac{1}{2}$, find the lowest common multiple of 3 and 2.

Multiples of 3 are: 3, **6**, 9, 12, . . .
Multiples of 2 are: 2, 4, **6**, 8, . . .
The lowest common multiple of 3 and 2 is 6.

Write equivalent fractions for $\frac{2}{3}$ and $\frac{1}{2}$ with 6 as denominator.

$$\frac{2}{3} = \frac{2 \times 2}{3 \times 2} = \frac{4}{6} \qquad\qquad \frac{1}{2} = \frac{1 \times 3}{2 \times 3} = \frac{3}{6}$$

$$\text{So,} \ \frac{2}{3} - \frac{1}{2} = \frac{4}{6} - \frac{3}{6}$$
$$= \frac{1}{6}$$

Practice

1. Subtract: $\frac{3}{2} - \frac{7}{10}$

The multiples of 2 are: _____

The multiples of 10 are: _____

The lowest common multiple of 2 and 10 is _____.

Use this as a common denominator.

$$\frac{3}{2} = \frac{3 \times \rule{1cm}{0.4pt}}{2 \times \rule{1cm}{0.4pt}} = \rule{1.5cm}{0.4pt} \qquad \text{So,} \ \frac{3}{2} - \frac{7}{10} = \rule{2cm}{0.4pt}$$

2. Subtract: $\frac{4}{9} - \frac{1}{3}$

The lowest common multiple of 9 and 3 is _____.

$$\frac{4}{9} - \frac{1}{3} = \rule{1.5cm}{0.4pt} - \rule{1.5cm}{0.4pt}$$

$$= \rule{1.5cm}{0.4pt}$$

3. Subtract.

a) $\dfrac{4}{5} - \dfrac{2}{3} =$ _____

b) $3 - \dfrac{2}{7} =$ _____ or _____

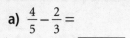

HINT

To subtract 2 mixed numbers:
- Subtract the whole numbers.
- Then subtract the fractions.

c) $2\dfrac{2}{3} - 1\dfrac{1}{4} =$ _____

d) $5\dfrac{7}{8} - 3\dfrac{3}{4} =$ _____

4. Susan and Ahmed entered a pie-eating contest.

Susan ate $\dfrac{5}{2}$ of pie. Ahmed ate $\dfrac{5}{3}$ of pie.

Who ate more? By how much?

5. Jie weeds $\dfrac{2}{5}$ of her garden on Friday, and $\dfrac{1}{3}$ on Saturday.

How much of the garden still needs to be weeded on Sunday?

Quick Review

You can think of multiplication as repeated addition.
This helps you to multiply fractions.

How many sevenths are in this sum?

$\frac{1}{7} + \frac{1}{7} + \frac{1}{7}$

You can write $\frac{1}{7} + \frac{1}{7} + \frac{1}{7}$ as: $3 \times \frac{1}{7}$

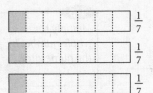

$3 \times \frac{1}{7} = \frac{3}{7}$

So, $\frac{1}{7} + \frac{1}{7} + \frac{1}{7} = 3 \times \frac{1}{7}$ or $\frac{3}{7}$

Practice

1. Write the addition as multiplication.

a) $\frac{3}{5} + \frac{3}{5} + \frac{3}{5} + \frac{3}{5} = $ _____ $\times \frac{3}{5}$

= _____

b) $\frac{5}{8} + \frac{5}{8} + \frac{5}{8} = $ _____ $\times \frac{5}{8}$

= _____

2. Write $5 \times \frac{2}{7}$ as a repeated addition.

Draw a picture to show your answer.

3. Write each multiplication as repeated addition.
Draw a picture to show your answer.

a) $3 \times \frac{1}{8}$

b) $4 \times \frac{2}{3}$

_____

_____

4. Multiply.

a) $5 \times \frac{1}{2} =$ _____

b) $\frac{3}{4} \times 3 =$ _____

c) $3 \times \frac{7}{10} =$ _____

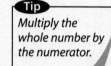
Tip
Multiply the whole number by the numerator.

d) $5 \times \frac{4}{5} =$ _____

e) $9 \times \frac{5}{9} =$ _____

f) $\frac{5}{6} \times 12 =$ _____

5. It takes Jerome $\frac{3}{4}$ h to cut a lawn.

Jerome cuts the grass for 5 neighbours.
How long does it take him to cut all the grass?

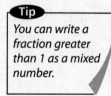
Tip
You can write a fraction greater than 1 as a mixed number.

_____

6. Harry practises basketball for $\frac{4}{3}$ h every night, 5 days a week.

For how many hours does Harry practise basketball in a week?

_____

Quick Review

➤ You can use Base Ten Blocks to multiply decimals.
To multiply 2.4×1.8, display the Base Ten Blocks as shown.
The flat represents 1.
The rod represents 0.1.
The small cube represents 0.01.
This picture shows the product
$$2.4 \times 1.8 = 1 + 1 + 0.8 + 0.8 + 0.4 + 0.32$$
$$= 4.32$$

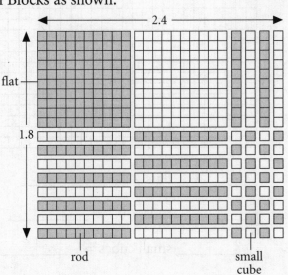

➤ You can multiply decimals the same
way you multiply whole numbers.
To multiply 2.4×1.8, multiply 24×18.

$$\begin{array}{r} 24 \\ \times\ 18 \\ \hline 432 \end{array}$$

Estimate to place the decimal point in the answer.
2.4×1.8 is about $2 \times 2 = 4$.
So, the product is 4.32.

Practice

1. Write a multiplication equation for each picture.
Each small square represents 0.01.

a)

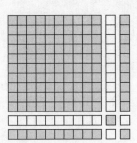

_____

b)

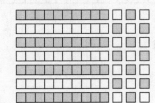

_____

2. Use Base Ten Blocks to find each product.
   Record your work on the grid.
   a) 2.6 × 1.3

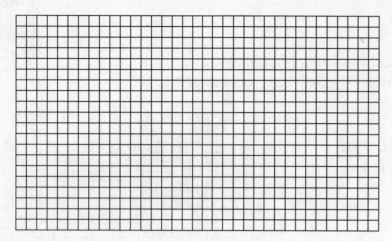

_____ flats × 1 = _____

_____ rods × 0.1 = _____

_____ small cubes = _____

The product is _____ + _____ + _____ = _____

b) 2.1 × 0.8

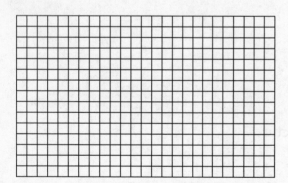

The product is _____.

c) 0.7 × 0.3

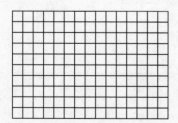

The product is _____.

3. Multiply. Estimate to place the decimal point in the answer.

a) 6.3×0.7

Multiply: 63×7

$$\begin{array}{r} 63 \\ \times\ 7 \\ \hline \end{array}$$

Estimate to place the decimal point.

$6.3 \times 0.7 =$ _____

b) 1.8×1.4

Multiply: 18×14

$1.8 \times 1.4 =$ _____

c) 4.8×6

d) 3.4×2.1

e) 0.4×1.4

$4.8 \times 6 =$ _____

$3.4 \times 2.1 =$ _____

$0.4 \times 1.4 =$ _____

4. A rectangular room measures 2.3 m by 3.2 m.
Find the area of the room.

_____

5. The product of 2 decimals is 0.24.
Write 3 pairs of decimals that give this product.

_____   _____   _____

Quick Review

Similar to the way you multiply decimals, you can divide decimals by thinking about the same operation with whole numbers.

To divide $5.6 \div 0.7$, you divide $56 \div 7 = 8$.
Estimate to place the decimal point in the answer.
$5.6 \div 0.7$ is about $6 \div 1 = 6$. So, $5.6 \div 0.7 = 8$

To divide $24.3 \div 1.2$, first divide $243 \div 12$.

```
         20.2 5
    12 | 243.00
         24
          30
          24
          60
          60
           0
```

Estimate to place the decimal point in the answer.
$24.3 \div 1.2$ is about $24 \div 1 = 24$.
So, $24.3 \div 1.2 = 20.25$.

Practice

1. Divide.

a) $17.4 \div 2.4$

```
    24 | 174.
```

b) $34.2 \div 3.6$

$17.4 \div 2.4$ is about

_____ ÷ _____ = _____

So, $17.4 \div 2.4 =$ _____   So, $34.2 \div 3.6 =$ _____

c) $89.9 \div 3.1 =$ _____   **d)** $15.3 \div 6.8 =$ _____

2. Divide. Round the quotient to the nearest tenth if necessary.

Tip
You may want to use a calculator to help with the division.

a) $5.14 \div 1.07 =$ _____

b) $95 \div 5.4 =$ _____

c) $80.96 \div 41.8 =$ _____

d) $381.5 \div 2.4 =$ _____

3. Sheldon rode his bicycle 53.4 km in 3 days.
What was his mean distance travelled per day?

H I N T

The mean is the average. It equals the sum divided by the number of items making up the sum.

_____

4. Nadine has a part-time job after school.
Suppose she earns $91.98 for working 12.6 hours.
How much does she earn per hour?

_____

5. The possible quotients for $72.09 \div 8.1$ are: 0.89, 89, 890, and 8.9.
Which number is correct? Explain how you know.

_____

_____

_____

6. The area of a rectangular room is approximately 47.3 m².
The width of the room is 5.4 m.
Find the length of the room.
Round your answer to 1 decimal place.

key to success

As you work through the Practice questions, ask:
• What have I learned?
• Do I understand?
• What am I not sure about?

_____

Quick Review

You can use the same order of operations for decimals as you can for whole numbers.

Here is the order of operations.
• Do the operations in brackets first.
• Then divide and multiply, in order, from left to right.
• Then add and subtract, in order, from left to right.

Practice

1. Evaluate.

   a) $1.2 + 3.1 \times 2 - (2.7 + 0.6) \div 3$ Calculate in brackets.

      = _____   Multiply and divide from left to right.

      = _____   Add and subtract from left to right.

      = _____

   b) $9.9 + 5 \times 4.6$ c) $(6.2 - 2.6) \div 2 =$ _____

      = _____

      = _____

2. Evaluate.

   a) $7 \times (6 + 7.1) =$ _____   b) $16 - 9.6 \div 3.2 =$ _____

   c) $5.8 + 12.3 \times 3 =$ _____   d) $4.9 + 17.6 \div 8 =$ _____

3. a) Evaluate each expression.

$(5.3 + 7.5) \times (3 - 1) =$ _____ $5.3 + 7.5 \times 3 - 1 =$ _____

b) The numbers and operations are the same in the two expressions in part a.
Explain why the results are different.

_____

_____

_____

_____

4. a) Evaluate each expression.

$7.2 \times 4.2 + 3.4 =$ _____ $(7.2 \times 4.2) + 3.4 =$ _____

b) Explain the results.

_____

_____

_____

5. Evaluate.

a) $3.6 \times 5 - 4.8 \div 4 + 10.2 =$ _____   **b)** $(8.4 + 3.6) \div 6 \times 10 - 9.5 \times 2 =$ _____

6. A radio station contest used this skill-testing question: $4 + 6 \times 1.3 - 2.4 \div 2$.
Grace said the answer was 10.6. Rob said the answer was 5.3.
Who was correct? How do you know?

_____

_____

_____

In Your Words

Here are some of the important mathematical words of this unit.
Build your own glossary by recording definitions and examples here. The first one is done for you.

equivalent fractions

Fractions that are equal in value but have

different numerators and denominators

For example, $\frac{2}{3} = \frac{4}{6} = \frac{10}{15}$

common denominator

_____

_____

_____

_____

_____

lowest common denominator

_____

_____

_____

_____

_____

_____

unit fraction

_____

_____

_____

_____

_____

_____

terminating decimal

_____

_____

_____

_____

_____

repeating decimal

_____

_____

_____

_____

_____

List other mathematical words you need to know.

_____

Unit Review

LESSON

4.1 **1.** Write the addition equation represented by the diagram.

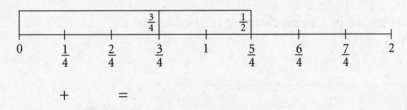

_____ + _____ = _____

4.2 **2.** Write the addition equation represented by the diagram.

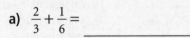

_____ + _____ = _____

4.3 **3.** Find a common denominator and add.

a) $\frac{2}{3} + \frac{1}{6} =$ _____

b) $\frac{2}{4} + \frac{3}{10} =$ _____

c) $3\frac{1}{4} + 1\frac{1}{2} =$ _____

d) $\frac{2}{3} + \frac{1}{9} + \frac{7}{9} =$ _____

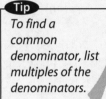

Tip

To find a common denominator, list multiples of the denominators.

4.4 **4.** A bread recipe calls for $\frac{2}{3}$ of a cup of water, and $\frac{1}{2}$ of a cup of milk.

How much more water is required than milk?

a) Describe how you use models to answer the question.

_____

_____

_____

b) How much more water is required than milk?

_____

_____

4.5 **5.** Subtract. Estimate first.

a) $\frac{5}{8} - \frac{1}{4} =$ _____

b) $\frac{3}{3} - \frac{3}{4} =$ _____

c) $4\frac{2}{5} - 3\frac{3}{10} =$ _____

4.6 **6.** Multiply.

a) $3 \times \frac{3}{4} =$ _____

b) $10 \times \frac{5}{7} =$ _____

7. Imshan spends $\frac{1}{4}$ h each day cleaning his bedroom.

How much time does he spend in a week cleaning his bedroom?

_____

4.7 **8.** Multiply.

a) $5 \times 2.7 =$ _____

b) $2.9 \times 0.8 =$ _____

c) $3.5 \times 3.2 =$ _____

d) $0.7 \times 0.5 =$ _____

> **Tip**
> Multiply or divide without the decimal point. Estimate to place the decimal point in the answer.

4.8 **9.** Divide. Round the quotient to the nearest tenth if necessary.

a) $8.7 \div 0.6 =$ _____

b) $5.7 \div 1.5 =$ _____

c) $43.1 \div 2.1 =$ _____

4.9 **10.** Evaluate.

a) $5.3 - 2.3 \times 2 =$ _____

b) $(67.2 + 12) \div 2.4 - 1.2 =$ _____

> **Tip**
> The order of operations with decimals is the same as with whole numbers.

UNIT 5

Data Management

Just for Fun

Secret Messages

> QSFO K WKX K PSCR: POON RSW PYB K NKI.
> DOKMR K WKX DY PSCR: POON RSW PYB K VSPODSWO.

Can you decipher this secret message?

Each letter in the original message has been replaced by another letter.
Each letter is replaced by the same letter every time.
No two letters are replaced by the same letter.
Each letter is shifted the same number of spaces.

Use the statistical data about how often each letter in the English alphabet is used.
Here is a table showing this information in a text of 1000 letters.

A	B	C	D	E	F	G	H	I	J	K	L	M	N	O	P	Q	R	S	T	U	V	W	X	Y	Z
73	9	30	44	130	28	16	35	74	2	3	35	25	78	74	27	3	77	63	93	27	13	16	5	19	1

Here are the frequencies of the letters in the secret message.

A	B	C	D	E	F	G	H	I	J	K	L	M	N	O	P	Q	R	S	T	U	V	W	X	Y	Z
0	2	2	3	0	1	0	0	1	0	9	0	1	3	8	7	1	5	7	0	0	1	5	2	3	0

Compare the two tables.
Shift the tallies so that the large and small frequencies from each table match up roughly.
Message letters O and P may correspond to English letters E and F, while message letters T and U may correspond to English letters J and K.
This would mean each letter has shifted 10 places.

Use this relation to decode the secret message.

_____

_____

97

Skills You'll Need

Calculating Mean, Median, and Mode

In a set of data that are numbers, the mean is $\dfrac{\text{Sum of all data values}}{\text{Number of data values}}$.

The median is the middle number when the numbers in a set of data are arranged in order from least to greatest.

If the number of data is even, the median is the mean of the 2 middle numbers.

The mode is the number that occurs most often in a set of data. There can be more than 1 mode or there can be no mode.

Example

Calculate the mean, median, and mode of this set of numbers:
11, 9, 12, 8, 11, 10, 11, 8

Solution

There are 8 numbers in the set.

$$\text{Mean} = \frac{11 + 9 + 12 + 8 + 11 + 10 + 11 + 8}{8} = \frac{80}{8} = 10$$

The numbers in order from least to greatest are: 8, 8, 9, $\boxed{10, 11,}$ 11, 11, 12

$$\text{Median} = \frac{10 + 11}{2} = \frac{21}{2} = 10.5$$

The number 11 occurs three times. So, the mode is 11.

✔ Check

1. Calculate the mean, median, and mode of each set of numbers.

a) 5, 8, 0, 2, 10, 2, 4, 1, 4

Mean = _____

= _____

The numbers from least to greatest are:

_____

Median = _____

Mode = _____

b) 14, 16, 13, 24, 18, 14

Mean = _____

= _____

The numbers from least to greatest are:

_____

Median = _____

Mode = _____

Quick Review

➤ Data collected by conducting a survey or an experiment are **primary data**.
Data you find in the library or using the Internet are **secondary data**.

➤ When you conduct a survey, the question you ask must be **unbiased**.
A **biased** question leads a person toward a particular answer.
The data collected are then unreliable.

For example, suppose you ask: "What is your favourite flower?"
The choices are:

A. tulip   B. rose   C. daffodil   D. other

More people tend to choose A, B, or C because the names are there.
To remove bias, leave the question open-ended with no choices given.

Practice

1. Data are collected by each survey method listed.
Classify the data as primary or secondary. The first one is done for you.

a) Ask every classmate to find the favourite subject of the class.   primary

b) Use your computer to find the most popular song of the week.   _____

c) Survey your neighbours to find the best restaurant in your area.   _____

d) Telephone different stores to find the lowest price for an appliance.   _____

e) Telephone Environment Canada to find a year's highest daily temperature. _____

2. Which survey question is unbiased? Explain.

A: "Which do you prefer for lunch: a pizza,
a hamburger, or fried chicken?"

B: "Would you prefer fried chicken for lunch to a
boring pizza or hamburger?"

HINT

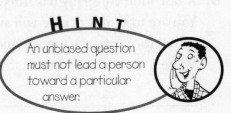

An unbiased question
must not lead a person
toward a particular
answer.

_____

_____

3. Sheila surveyed her classmates. She asked this question:
"What type of music do you like to listen to: Rock, Country, Classical, or Other?"
Is her question biased? If so, write an unbiased question.

_____

_____

4. House owners were asked this question:
"Which type of power generation do you prefer: hydroelectric or nuclear power that produces radioactive dust?"
How is the question biased? Rewrite the question so it is unbiased.

_____

_____

_____

_____

5. The Student Council asked this biased question:
"Will you attend the next ever-popular and fun school dance?"

a) What would be an unbiased question to ask?

_____

b) Why do you think the Student Council asked a biased question?

_____

_____

6. A fast-food company has hired you to do a survey.
You are to find if people will switch from eating french fries to eating the company's new potato product.
Write 3 survey questions that would give the company accurate results.

> **Tip**
> Survey questions need to be asked in the correct order.

_____

_____

_____

_____

Quick Review

➤ You can record data in different ways.
You can use a table, a bar graph, or a pictograph.

➤ The table shows the results of a telephone survey to find Canadians' favourite ice-cream flavour.

Ice-Cream Flavour	Tally	Frequency
Vanilla	~~IIII~~ ~~IIII~~ II	12
Chocolate	~~IIII~~ ~~IIII~~ ~~IIII~~ ~~IIII~~	20
Strawberry	~~IIII~~ ~~IIII~~ ~~IIII~~ ~~IIII~~ II	22
Chocolate chip	~~IIII~~ I	6

➤ You can use a bar graph or a pictograph to display the data.

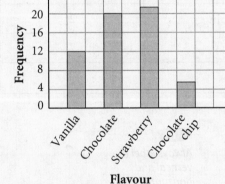

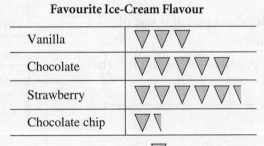

Favourite Ice-Cream Flavour

Key: ▽ represents 4 people

Practice

1. a) Complete the table that shows the type of pets in a home.

Pet	Tally	Frequency (Homes)
Bird	~~IIII~~ II	
Cat	~~IIII~~ ~~IIII~~ II	
Dog	~~IIII~~ ~~IIII~~ ~~IIII~~ II	
Hamster	IIII	

KEY TO SUCCESS

Make notes in your notebook about the special features and the appropriate uses of each type of graph for quick reference.

b) How many homes were surveyed? _____

c) Draw a bar graph to display the data.

Homes with Pets

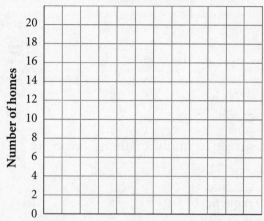

Pet

2. The table shows the results of a class survey on the main use of the Internet.

a) Draw a bar graph to display the data.

b) How many students were surveyed?

_____ students were surveyed.

c) What is the most popular use of the Internet?

The most popular use of the Internet

is for _____.

Main Use of Internet

Use	Number of Students
Instant Messaging	12
Research	10
Shopping	2
Music	7
Games	5

Main Use of Internet

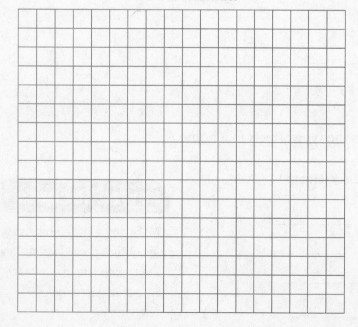

Tip

Always label the vertical and horizontal axes on a bar graph.

3. Draw a pictograph for the data.

Type of Music CD Sold	Number
Rock	12
R&B	18
Country	10
Classical	16
Jazz	14

Type of Music CD Sold

Rock	
R&B	
Country	
Classical	
Jazz	

Key: ⊙ represents 4 CDs

a) What is the total number of CDs sold? _____

b) How would the pictograph change if ⊙ represented 2 CDs?

_____

_____

4. The table records the life expectancy (how long an animal can live) of some animals.

Life Expectancy of Animals

Animal	Life Expectancy (years)
Grizzly bear	25
Cheetah	14
Elephant	35
Giraffe	10
Lion	15

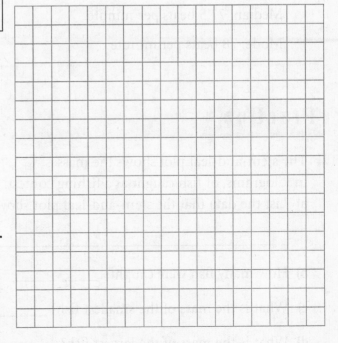

HINT

On the grid, choose a vertical scale that will fit all data in the table on the graph.

a) Draw a bar graph to show the life expectancy of the animals listed.

b) A zoo wants to buy an animal that will live for a long time. Which animal should the zoo consider buying?

The zoo should consider buying

_____ .

Quick Review

➤ A **stem-and-leaf plot** is a way to display data.
Each number in the data is split into its "stem" part and "leaf" part.
For two-digit numbers, the tens digits are the stems and the ones
digits are the leaves.

This set of data shows the normal heart
rates of Class 7-C in a school.

Heart Rates in Beats per Minute				
80	70	87	89	78
75	68	74	80	72
82	74	75	69	79
77	78	76	78	81

➤ To make a stem-and-leaf plot for the data,
order the numbers from least to greatest.
Since each number is a two-digit number,
the tens digit is the stem and the ones
digit is the leaf.

Heart Rates of Class 7-C in Beats per Minute

Stem	Leaf
6	8 9
7	0 2 4 4 5 5 6 7 8 8 8 9
8	0 0 1 2 7 9

➤ You can find the **range**, **median**, and **mode** of the data from
a stem-and-leaf plot.
For the above leaf-and-stem plot, the heart rates range from 68 to 89.

Range: 89 – 68 = 21 beats per minute

Median: 77.5 beats per minute

Mode: 78 beats per minute

Practice

1. The stem-and-leaf plot shows the masses,
in kilograms, of fish caught at a fishing contest.
   a) List the data that the stem-and-leaf plot shows.

   _____

   b) How many fish were caught? _____

   c) What is the mass of the smallest fish? _____

   d) What is the mass of the largest fish? _____

Masses of Fish (kg)

Stem	Leaf
1	2 7
2	5 6 8
3	0 4 9
4	1

104

2. The stem-and-leaf plot shows the ages of members of the local chess club.

Ages of Chess Club Members

Stem	Leaf
0	7 8
1	0 0 1 2 2 4 6 7 9
2	0 1 1 4
3	8 9
4	0 8
5	2
6	5

a) How many members are under 10 years old? _____

b) How many members are teenagers? List all their ages.

_____

c) How many members are over 50 years old? _____

d) How old is the oldest member? _____

3. Megan measured the heights of 12 young pine trees near her home. She recorded their heights in centimetres:

102, 105, 110, 115, 118, 120, 125, 134, 135, 145, 153, 158

a) Find the range of the heights of the trees. Show your calculation.

_____

b) Complete this stem-and-leaf plot of the data.

Heights of Trees in Centimetres

Stem	Leaf
10	2
11	0
12	
13	
14	
15	

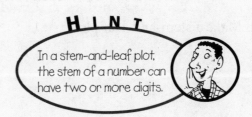

HINT

In a stem-and-leaf plot, the stem of a number can have two or more digits.

c) What are the place values of the digits in the stems?

_____

d) What is the place value of the digits in the leaves?

_____

e) Find the median height. _____

4. Zachary was invited to many birthday parties last year. He spent these amounts on the gifts:

$8, $14, $20, $12, $23, $18, $10, $16, $12, $20, $12, $15

a) Find the range of the data. _____

b) Make a stem-and-leaf plot.

c) Find the median and the mode.

Median: _____

Mode: _____

5. Ethel recorded the gas consumption, in litres per 100 km, of 10 cars.

5.6, 7.1, 6.1, 6.3, 7.1, 7.1, 6.1, 7.8, 4.7, 7.5

a) Make a stem-and-leaf plot.

b) What is the place value of the digits in the stems? _____

c) What is the place value of the digits in the leaves? _____

d) Write 3 things you know from looking at the plot.

_____

_____

Quick Review

➤ A **line graph** shows changes in data over time. This line graph shows the changes in diameter of an oak tree over the years.

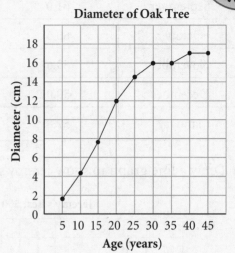

Diameter of Oak Tree

➤ The horizontal axis represents the age of the tree. The vertical axis represents the diameter in centimetres. As the tree gets older, the diameter of the tree increases.

➤ You can use the line graph to find values between data points. For example, at the age of 18, the diameter of the oak tree is about 10 cm.

➤ You may also make predictions for values in future years. For example, the diameter of the tree at the age of 50 will be approximately 18 cm.

Practice

1. The line graph shows movie ticket sales at the Statsville Theatre.

   a) On which day do the most people go to the movies at Statsville?

   _____

   b) On which day do the fewest people go to the movies at Statsville?

   _____

   c) About how many tickets were sold on Thursday?

   _____

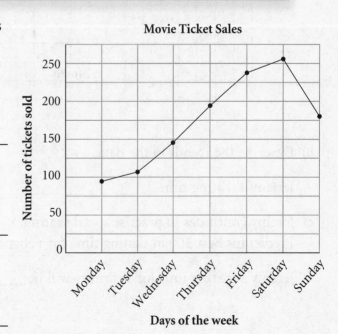

Movie Ticket Sales

2. Jeremy keeps track of his best speed skating time for 500 m every month.
The table shows his record for seven months.

Best Speed Skating Times for 500 m	
Month	Time (s)
September	61.0
October	60.5
November	59.6
December	59.0
January	57.8

a) Draw a line graph to show Jeremy's speed skating times.

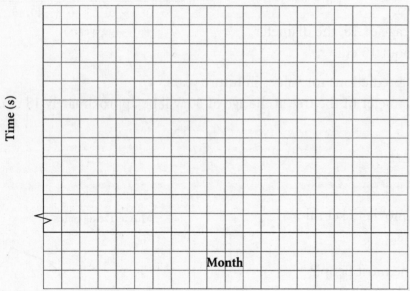

Jeremy's Best 500 m Skating Times

b) Describe the trends in the data.

Jeremy's skating time _____ from September to January.

c) Jeremy continues to practise speed skating.
Predict his best 500 m skating time for February.

Jeremy's skating time for February will be _____.

3. The table shows the number of students enrolled in a college.

Student Enrollment

Year	Number
1995	125
1997	155
1999	210
2001	185
2003	175
2005	150

a) Draw a line graph to show the student enrollment over the 6 years.

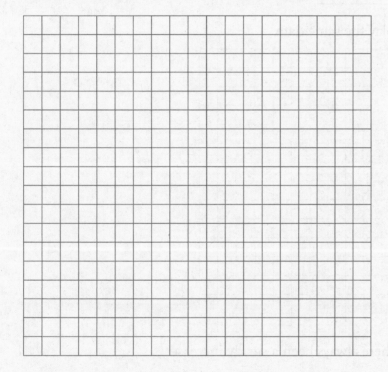

b) During which period is the increase in enrollment the greatest?

The increase was greatest from _____ to _____.

c) Assume the trend of the student enrollment continues.
About how many students will be enrolled in 2007?

In 2007, about _____ students will be enrolled.

4. The table and bar graph show the amount of carbon dioxide released into the atmosphere as a result of human activities.

Carbon Dioxide Released	
Year	Carbon Dioxide (million tonnes)
1970	4000
1975	5400
1980	5000
1985	5400
1990	6100
1995	6200

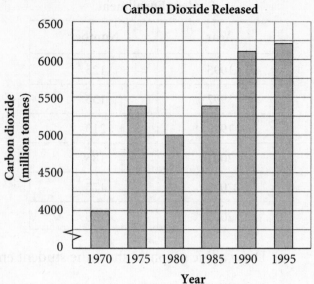

a) Draw a line graph to display the same data.

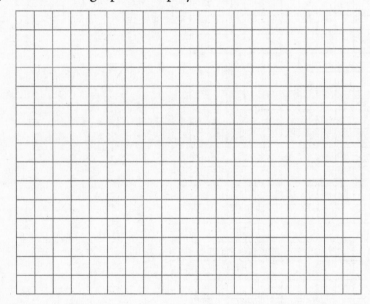

b) Describe the trend. Has there always been a steady increase?

_____

c) Predict the amount of carbon dioxide released into the atmosphere in 2010.

_____

d) Write a question you could answer using the line graph but not the bar graph. Answer your question.

_____

_____

_____

Tip

There are no values between bars on a bar graph.

Quick Review

➤ The mean, median, and mode are all measures of central tendency
   of a set of data.
   However, not all of them describe the data in the same way.

   Zoe's hamster has had several litters of babies.
   Zoe recorded the number of babies in each litter: 17, 16, 15, 12, 5, 5, 4

   There are 7 numbers in the set.

   Mean: $\dfrac{17 + 16 + 15 + 12 + 5 + 5 + 4}{7} = \dfrac{74}{7}$, which is about 10.6

   Zoe's hamster has a mean of 10.6 babies in a litter.

   The numbers of babies in order from least to greatest are: 4, 5, 5, 12, 15, 16, 17
   The middle number is 12.
   So, the median is 12 babies in a litter.

   The number 5 occurs two times.
   So, the mode is 5 babies in a litter.

   Four of the seven litters have numbers greater than 5.
   So, the mode is not representative of the data.

   The median is one of the data.
   The number of data greater than the median equals the number of data
   less than the median.
   So, the median would be the best measure of central tendency
   used to describe the "average" litter size of the hamster.

Practice

1. Kate scored these points in her last six basketball games: 7, 8, 10, 5, 15, 15
   a) Find her mean, median, and mode scores.

   Mean: _____   Median: _____   Mode: _____

   b) Which measure of central tendency should Kate use to show her coach that she is
      valuable player?
      Give a reason for your choice.

   Kate should use the _____ because _____.

2. There are five numbers in a set of data.
The two modes are 0 and 2.
The median and the mean are both 2.
Find the 5 numbers.

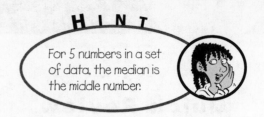

H I N T

For 5 numbers in a set of data, the median is the middle number.

_____

3. A cereal manufacturer says that each box of cereal has an average of 50 g of raisins.
A random check is made on 20 boxes.
The table shows the results.

Raisins per 400 g Box	
Amount (g)	**Number of Boxes**
48	1
49	4
50	4
51	6
52	5

a) Calculate the mean, median, and mode of the data.

Mean: _____

Median: _____

Mode: _____

b) Is the manufacturer's claim acceptable?
Justify your answer.

_____

4. The term "average" can refer to the mean, median, or mode.
Which average is likely being referred to in each case?

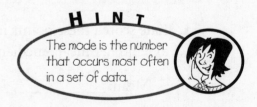

H I N T

The mode is the number that occurs most often in a set of data.

a) The average Canadian sleeps 8.3 hours per night. _____

b) The average Canadian owns 2 computers. _____

c) The average Canadian is on the Internet 2 hours per day. _____

5. A radio station is having a weekly Song War between the top two hit songs.
Listeners have all week to call in their votes.
Each day, the station rounds the number of calls it receives to the nearest 10
and records the number of calls.

Votes for Song A and Song B		
Day	Song A	Song B
Monday	120	200
Tuesday	100	130
Wednesday	130	90
Thursday	250	80
Friday	100	200

a) Find the mean, median, and mode votes of Song A.

Mean: _____

Median: _____

Mode: _____

b) Find the mean, median, and mode votes of Song B.

Mean: _____

Median: _____

Mode: _____

c) Which song is more popular? Explain your choice.

_____

_____

_____

_____

Quick Review

➤ Sometimes, a graph that shows correct data may still be misleading.
Both of these graphs show the same data.

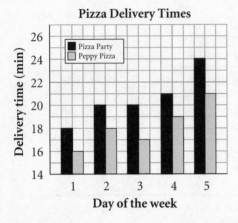

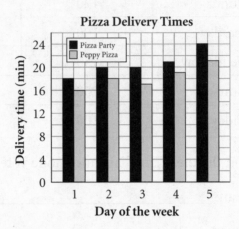

➤ The graph on the left is misleading.
It does not start with 0 on the vertical scale.
There is a big difference in the lengths of the bars representing the delivery times.
It suggests that Peppy Pizza delivers pizzas much faster than Pizza Party.
On some days, it looks like Peppy Pizza could be twice as fast.

➤ The graph on the right has the vertical scale starting at 0.
The lengths of the bars are now at the correct ratio.
The difference between bars is much smaller.
Peppy Pizza is faster but not twice as fast.

Practice

1. Why is this diagram misleading? Explain.

Burger Shack   Organically Beef

Calories: 555   539

Organically Beef — The healthier choice!

_____

_____

2. Which of these two graphs is misleading? Explain why it is misleading.

Tip

The difference between values looks different when you change the scale on a graph.

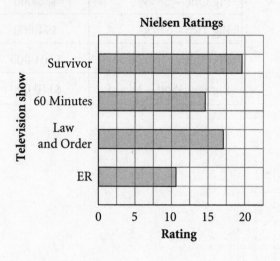

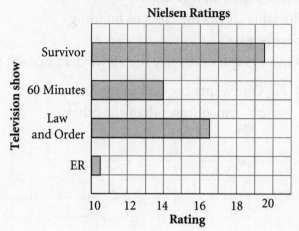

_____

_____

_____

3. The table shows the ranking of two baseball teams over the first half of the season.

Number of Games	Batty Bears	Pitchy Panthers
5	1	10
10	1	9
15	2	8
20	6	4
25	10	2

a) The local newspaper for the Batty Bears prints a story using this graph. How does it mislead the readers?

_____

_____

_____

_____

_____

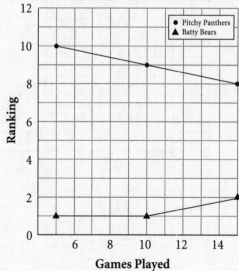

115

4. In the modern day *Three Little Pigs*, the pigs and the wolf hired contractors to build their new houses. The table shows the costs of building these houses.

Draw a graph to display the above data in each way:

Builder	Cost of Home
Pig One – Straw	$85 000
Pig Two – Sticks	$94 000
Pig Three – Brick	$104 000
Big Bad Wolf – Wood	$110 000

a) Pig One wants the cost of his house to look much lower than the others.

b) The Big Bad Wolf wants an accurate representation of the costs.

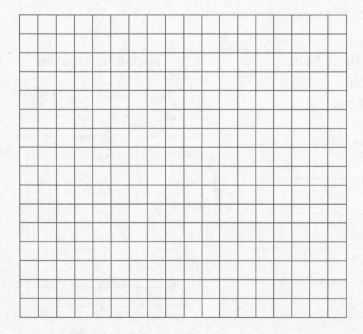

116

In Your Words

Here are some of the important mathematical words of this unit.
Build your own glossary by recording definitions and examples here. The first one is done for you.

bias _an emphasis on characteristics that are not typical of an entire population_
For example, bias can result from the wording of a question.

bar graph _____

pictograph _____

stem-and-leaf plot _____

mean _____

median _____

List other mathematical words you need to know.

_____

Unit Review

LESSON

5.1 **1.** Patrick wants to find out which chocolate bars would sell best in his school store.
He designed this survey question.
"Are Jupiter and Caramel Dream your favourite chocolate bars? If not, which ones are?"
Is this question biased? If it is, rewrite the question so it is unbiased.

_____

_____

5.2 **2.** Reid wants to find out how many sick leave days he should allow for his staff.
He recorded how often his staff visited the doctor in the past 6 months.

Number of Doctor Visits	0	1	2	3	4
Number of Staff	8	4	23	14	5

a) Draw a pictograph for the data. Use the letter "V" to represent 2 staff.

b) What is the minimum number of sick leave days in a year Reid should
allow for his staff?

_____

5.3 **3.** Radar equipment has been set up to clock the speeds of cars on a highway.
Here are the speeds of 20 cars.

Speeds of 20 Cars on Highway 100 (km/h)									
104	110	124	108	105	115	118	118	125	130
121	114	116	102	124	128	120	101	118	113

What is the range of the data? _____

4. **a)** Make a stem-and-leaf plot for the data in Question 3.

b) Which digits of the data are the stems?

_____

c) Which digits of the data are the leaves?

_____

5.4 **5.** The table shows the winning times of the 400-m race at a School Athletic Meet for boys and girls.

a) Draw a line graph to show the winning times for a 400-m race for boys and girls.

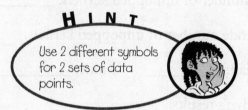

HINT

Use 2 different symbols for 2 sets of data points.

b) Predict the winning times for boys and for girls in 2006.

The winning time for boys will

be about _____ .

The winning time for girls will

be about _____ .

c) In about what year will the winning times be the same?

_____

Winning Times for 400 m		
Year	Boys (s)	Girls (s)
1994	85.4	93.4
1996	84.0	96.7
1998	83.4	96.1
2000	83.6	95.5
2002	83.0	94.0
2004	83.2	92.4

6. For a science project, Jocelyn counted the number of popcorn kernels that did not pop in 6 equal-sized packages of different popcorn brands.
She recorded her results in this table.

Brand	Number of Unpopped Kernels
TopPop	14
Popcorn Plenty	24
SmartPop	11
SnackTime	12
Kernel Jack	22
No-Na-Me	19

a) Which brand of popcorn has the fewest unpopped kernels? _____

b) Which brand has the greatest number of unpopped kernels? _____

c) Find the mean, median, and mode number of unpopped kernels.

Mean: _____   Median: _____   Mode: _____

d) Draw a bar graph to show Jocelyn's results.

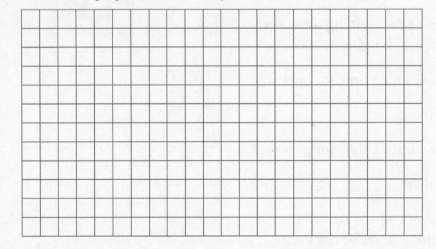

e) If you were trying to promote the SmartPop brand as "the popcorn that pops the most," would you use the mean, median, or mode? Just your answer.

_____

f) How could you present the data so that SmartPop looks significantly better than the rest of the brands?

_____

_____

Just for Fun

Card Pile-Up

Put the cards in a pile using these clues.

1. The hearts are somewhere between the 6 of clubs and the 6 of spades.
2. The 7 is somewhere between the ace of hearts and the 5 of hearts.
3. The diamond is somewhere above the club and below the 5.

List the cards in order.

_____

_____

_____

_____

Price for 2

An item is sold at this price:
The price for 1 is 33¢.
The price for 33 is 66¢.
The price for 133 is 99¢.
What could the item be?

_____

What would be the price for 2?

_____

Make a Chain

A Game for 2

You will need 12 counters of the same colour.
Your partner will need 12 counters of a different colour.

Take turns placing one of your counters on the grid.
The first player to make a line of same-colour counters
from one side of the grid to the opposite side wins.
The lines can have horizontal and vertical segments.

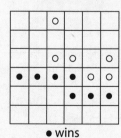

● wins

Skills You'll Need

Perimeter and Area of a Rectangle

Perimeter is the distance around a figure.
Area is the amount of surface a figure covers.

Example

a) Find the perimeter and area of the square.

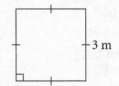
3 m

b) Find the perimeter and area of the rectangle.

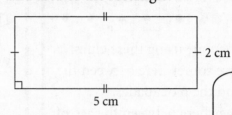
2 cm
5 cm

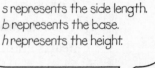
s represents the side length.
b represents the base.
h represents the height.

Solution

a) Perimeter, $P = 4s$
Substitute $s = 3$.
$P = 4 \times 3 = 12$
The perimeter is 12 m.

Area, $A = s^2$
Substitute $s = 3$.
$A = 3^2 = 9$
The area is 9 m².

b) Perimeter, $P = 2(b + h)$
Substitute $b = 5$ and $h = 2$.
$P = 2(5 + 2) = 14$
The perimeter is 14 cm.

Area, $A = bh$
Substitute $b = 5$ and $h = 2$.
$A = 5 \times 2 = 10$
The area is 10 cm².

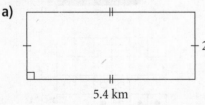 **Check**

1. Find the perimeter and area of each figure.

a)

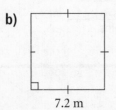
2.0 km
5.4 km

$P = 2(b + h)$

$= 2(\underline{\hspace{1cm}} + \underline{\hspace{1cm}})$

$= \underline{\hspace{1cm}}$

Perimeter = \underline{\hspace{2cm}}

$A = bh$

$= \underline{\hspace{1cm}} \times \underline{\hspace{1cm}}$

$= \underline{\hspace{1cm}}$

Area = \underline{\hspace{2cm}}

b)

7.2 m

Perimeter = \underline{\hspace{2cm}}   Area = \underline{\hspace{2cm}}

122

Quick Review

➤ You can rearrange a parallelogram to form a rectangle.
They have the same area.

➤ The formula for the area of a parallelogram is the same as for the area of a rectangle:
Area = base × height, or $A = bh$

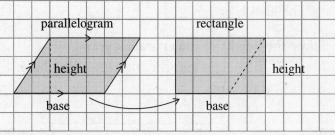

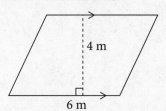

4 m

6 m

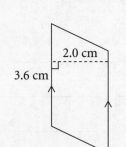

2.0 cm

3.6 cm

$A = bh$
Substitute $b = 6$ and $h = 4$.
$A = 6 \times 4$
$\quad = 24$
The area is 24 m².

$A = bh$
Substitute $b = 3.6$ and $h = 2.0$.
$A = 3.6 \times 2.0$
$\quad = 7.2$
The area is 7.2 cm².

Practice

1. Find the area of each parallelogram.

a)
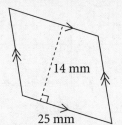

14 mm

25 mm

$A = bh$
Substitute $b = $ _____
and $h = $ _____.
$A = $

The area is _____.

b)
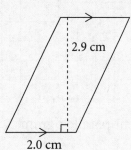

2.9 cm

2.0 cm

KEY TO SUCCESS

• Record formulas in your journal so that they can be found easily.
• Write an example of how to use each formula.

The area is _____.

123

2. Find the area of each parallelogram.

a)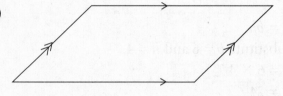

b)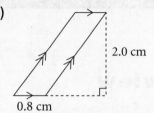

The area is _____.   The area is _____.

3. Draw the height of each parallelogram.
Measure the height and the corresponding base.
Then find the area.

Tip
*You can use a protractor
to draw a line
perpendicular to the base.*

a)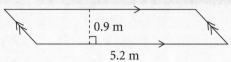

b)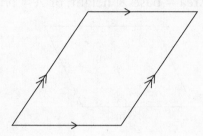

Height = _____ cm   Height = _____

Base = _____ cm   Base = _____

Area = _____ cm²   Area = _____

4.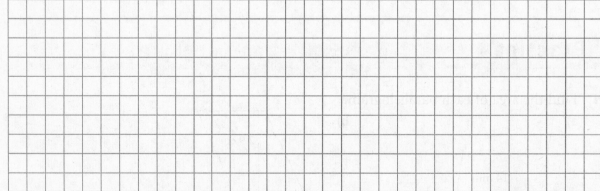

a) On the grid, draw 3 different parallelograms with base 6 units and
height 2 units.
Find the area of each parallelogram.

Tip
*The height can be
drawn outside the
parallelogram.*

_____

_____

b) Draw a parallelogram with base 3 units and height 2 units.
Find its area.

Area of new parallelogram = _____

How is the area changed? _____

c) Draw a parallelogram with base 6 units and height 4 units.
Find its area.

Area of new parallelogram = _____

How is the area changed? _____

5. The area and height of each parallelogram are given.
Find the measure of the base in each parallelogram.

a)

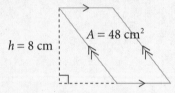

b)

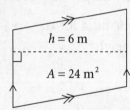

Area = base × height

48 = _____ × 8

Base = _____ cm

Base = _____

6. Jamie makes a road through his wooded lot.
What is the area of the lot that has trees? Show your work.

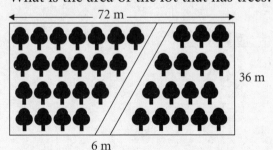

H I N T

Subtract the area of the road from the total area of the lot to find the area of the lot that has trees.

Quick Review

➤ This parallelogram has been divided into 2 congruent triangles.
So, the area of one triangle is $\frac{1}{2}$ the area of the parallelogram.

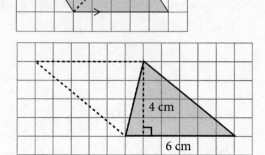

➤ To find the area of a triangle with base 6 cm and height 4 cm, complete a parallelogram on one side of the triangle.

➤ The area of the parallelogram is:
$A = $ base $\times$ height
$A = 6 \times 4 = 24$
The area of the parallelogram is 24 cm².
So, the area of the triangle is: $\frac{1}{2}$ of 24 cm² = 12 cm²

➤ You can use this formula for the area of a triangle.
Area $= \frac{1}{2}$ base $\times$ height
$A = \frac{1}{2} bh$
or $A = bh \div 2$
or $A = \frac{bh}{2}$

Practice

1. Find the area of each triangle.

a)

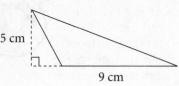

$A = \dfrac{bh}{2}$

$A =$

_____

$=$

_____

The area is _____ cm².

b)

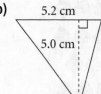

$A = \dfrac{bh}{2}$

$A =$

_____

$=$

_____

The area is _____ cm².

2. Find the area of each triangle.

a)

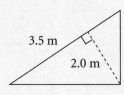

3.5 m

2.0 m

_____

_____

_____

b)

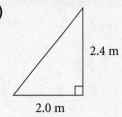

2.4 m

2.0 m

_____

_____

_____

3. Measure and label the base and height of each triangle in centimetres. Then calculate the area.

a)

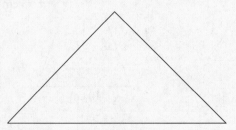

Area = _____

b)

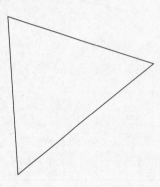

Area = _____

c)

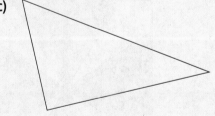

Area = _____

HINT

In a right triangle, 1 side is the base and 1 side is the height.

4. Draw 3 different triangles each with base 5 units and height 4 units.

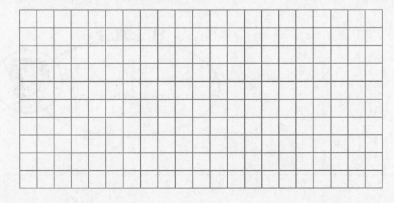

HINT

You can draw many different triangles with the same base and height.

5. Draw 3 different triangles each with area 12 square units.

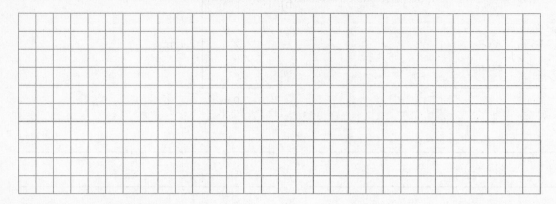

6. The area of each triangle is given.
Find the height of each triangle.

a)

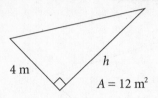

4 m
h
A = 12 m^2

b)

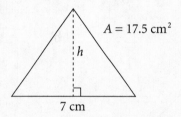

A = 17.5 cm^2
h
7 cm

c)

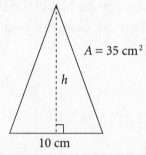

A = 35 cm^2
h
10 cm

Area = $\dfrac{bh}{2}$

$12 = \dfrac{4 \times h}{2}$

Height = _____

Height = _____

Height = _____

7. Bernice makes this design on a square sheet of paper.
The paper has a side length of 20 cm.
Each triangle has a base of 12 cm and a height of 10 cm.
Find the area of the white part of the design.
Show your work.

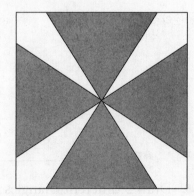

H I N T

Subtract the areas of
the shaded parts from
the area of the square
sheet of paper.

Quick Review

➤ A **trapezoid** is a 4-sided polygon with at least one pair of parallel sides.

➤ You can find the area of a trapezoid by dividing it into other figures. There are 3 ways to find the area of this trapezoid.

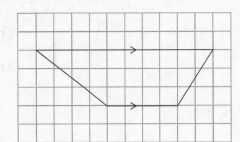

➤ Make 2 triangles.

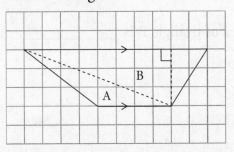

Area of trapezoid = area of triangle A
+ area of triangle B

➤ Make 1 triangle and a parallelogram.

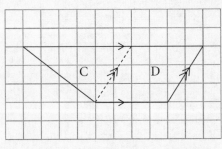

Area of trapezoid = area of triangle C
+ area of parallelogram D

➤ Make 2 triangles and a rectangle.

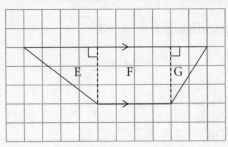

Area of trapezoid = area of triangle E
+ area of rectangle F
+ area of triangle G

➤ To find the perimeter of a trapezoid, add the side lengths.

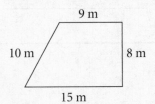

Perimeter = 9 m + 8 m + 15 m + 10 m = 42 m
The perimeter is 42 m.

1. Find the area of each trapezoid by dividing it into 2 triangles.

a)

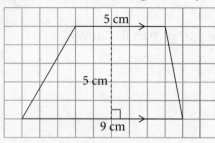

Area of triangle A: $A = \dfrac{bh}{2}$

$A =$ _____

The area of triangle A is _____.

Area of triangle B:

Area of trapezoid:

_____ + _____ = _____

The area of triangle B is _____.

b)

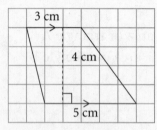

Area of trapezoid:

_____

2. Find the area of this trapezoid by dividing it into 1 triangle and a parallelogram. Show your work.

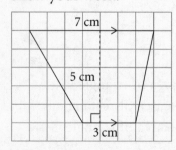

Area of parallelogram: $A = bh$

$A =$ _____

The area is _____.

Area of triangle: $A =$ _____

$A =$ _____

Area of trapezoid:

_____

3. Find the area of the trapezoid.
Show your work.

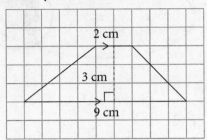

Area of trapezoid:

_____

4. Find the area of each trapezoid by dividing it into 2 triangles and a rectangle.
Show your work.

a)

Area of each triangle: $A = \dfrac{bh}{2}$

$A =$ _____

The area is _____.

Area of trapezoid:

_____

Area of square: $A = s^2$

$A =$ _____

The area is _____.

b)

Area of trapezoid:

_____

5. Find the area and perimeter of each trapezoid.

a)

10 cm

13 cm   15 cm

12 cm

24 cm

HINT

To find the area of a trapezoid, divide it into other figures.

Area = _____

Perimeter = _____

b)

6 m

10 m   18 m

10 m

Area = _____

Perimeter = _____

c)

7.0 cm

6.0 cm   5.4 cm

5.0 cm

12.3 cm

Area = _____

Perimeter = _____

6. Fatima is painting this cardboard cutout for her class play. The cutout is a trapezoid 3 m tall. It has a square opening. What is the area of cardboard that Fatima needs to paint? Show your work.

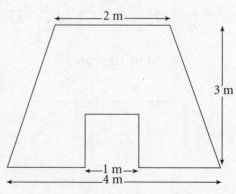

2 m

3 m

1 m

4 m

Quick Review

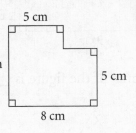
Here are 2 ways to find the area of this irregular figure.

➤ Divide the figure into smaller figures.

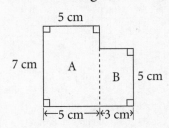

Area of rectangle A: 5 cm × 7 cm = 35 cm²
Area of rectangle B: 3 cm × 5 cm = 15 cm²
The area of the figure is: 35 cm² + 15 cm² = 50 cm²

➤ Draw a rectangle around the figure.

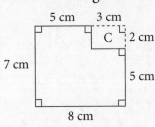

Area of the large rectangle: 7 cm × 8 cm = 56 cm²
Area of rectangle C: 3 cm × 2 cm = 6 cm²
The area of the figure is: 56 cm² − 6 cm² = 50 cm²

➤ To find the perimeter of the figure, add the side lengths.

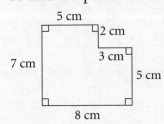

Perimeter = 5 cm + 2 cm + 3 cm + 5 cm + 8 cm + 7 cm
= 30 cm
The perimeter is 30 cm.

Practice

1. Find the perimeter of this figure. Show your work.

a)

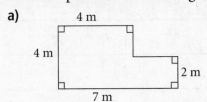

HINT
Start by finding the lengths of the unmarked sides.

2. Find the area of each figure by dividing it into smaller figures. Show your work.

a)

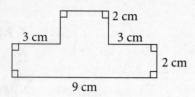

The area of the figure is _____.

b)

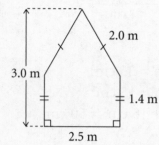

The area of the figure is _____.

c)

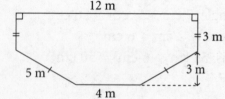

The area of the figure is _____.

3. Find the perimeter of each figure in question 2.
Show your work.

a) _____

_____

b) _____

_____

c) _____

_____

4. Find the area of each figure by drawing a rectangle around it. Show your work.

a)

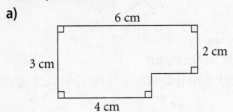

b)

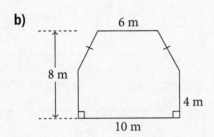

5. Caitlin plans to have new carpet installed in her family room. How many square metres of carpet will she need?

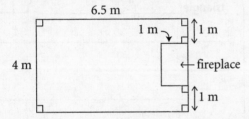

6. Loki has 18 patio tiles. Each tile has an area of 1 m².
He wants to build a T-shaped patio using all the tiles.

a) Draw 4 different designs for Loki's patio. Label the designs A, B, C, and D.

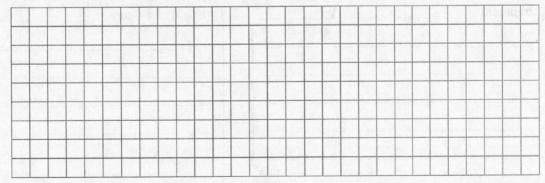

b) Find the perimeter of each patio you drew.

A: _____   B: _____   C: _____   D: _____

In Your Words

Here are some of the important mathematical words of this unit.
Build your own glossary by recording definitions and examples here. The first one is done for you.

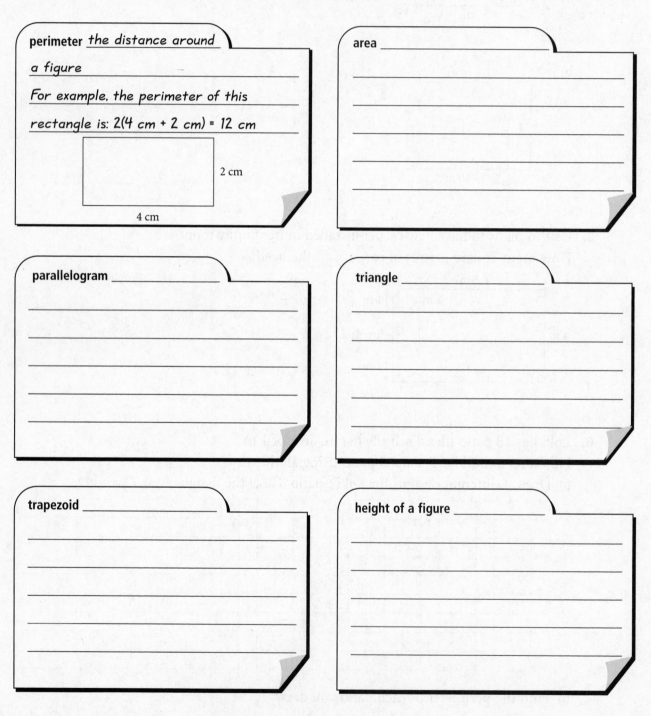

perimeter *the distance around*
a figure
For example, the perimeter of this
rectangle is: 2(4 cm + 2 cm) = 12 cm

2 cm

4 cm

area _____
_____
_____
_____
_____
_____

parallelogram _____
_____
_____
_____
_____

triangle _____
_____
_____
_____
_____

trapezoid _____
_____
_____
_____
_____

height of a figure _____
_____
_____
_____
_____

List other mathematical words you need to know.

_____

Unit Review

6.1 **1.** Draw, measure, and label a height of
each parallelogram.
Then calculate the area of each parallelogram.
Show your work.

Tip

A base can be any side of a parallelogram.
The corresponding height is perpendicular to the base.

a)

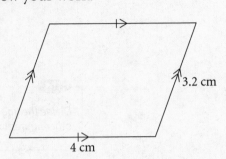

4 cm

3.2 cm

b)

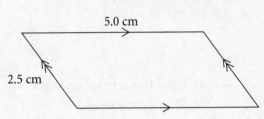

5.0 cm

2.5 cm

Base = _____

Height = _____

Area = base × height

Area = _____ × _____ = _____

The area is _____.

_____

6.2 **2.** Find the area of each triangle. Show your work.

a)

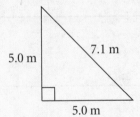

5.0 m

7.1 m

5.0 m

b)

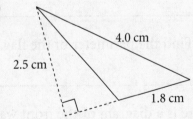

4.0 cm

2.5 cm

1.8 cm

_____   _____

6.3

3. Find the area and perimeter of this trapezoid. Show your work.

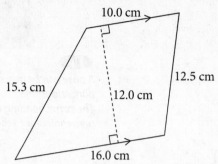

10.0 cm

15.3 cm

12.5 cm

12.0 cm

16.0 cm

4. a) Find the area of each section of this flag.
Show your work.

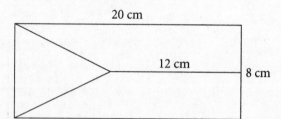

20 cm

12 cm

8 cm

Tip
Divide the flag into other figures to help.

b) Find the area of the whole flag.

_____

c) Find the perimeter of the flag.

_____

6.4

5. Here is a diagram of the front wall of a doghouse.
What is the area of the wall, not including the doorway? Show your work.

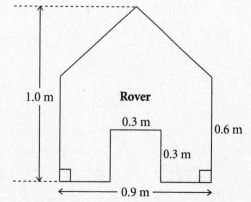

1.0 m

Rover

0.3 m

0.6 m

0.3 m

0.9 m

Geometry

Just for Fun

Geometry Crossword

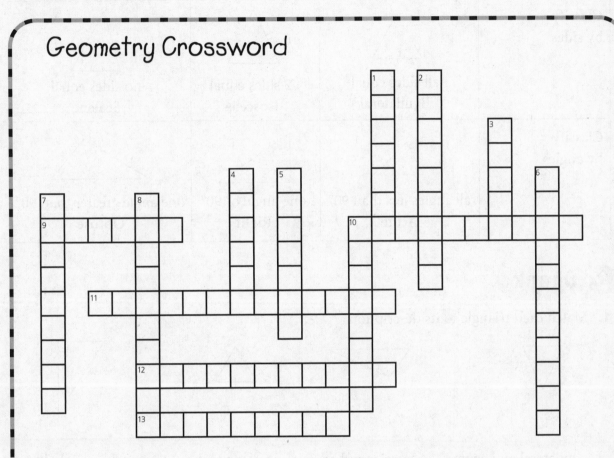

Across

9. A type of dot paper
10. A transformation in which you flip a figure in a mirror line
11. A quadrilateral with both pairs of opposite sides parallel
12. A transformation in which you slide a figure in a straight line
13. A quadrilateral with four right angles

Down

1. A triangle with all sides different
2. A triangle with two equal sides
3. A triangle with one 90° angle
4. A triangle with one angle greater than 90°
5. A six-sided polygon
6. The numbers in an ordered pair that locate a point on a grid
7. A type of dot paper
8. You use this to measure angles.
10. A transformation in which you turn a figure about a fixed point

Skills You'll Need

Classifying Triangles

You can classify triangles by their sides, or by their angles.

Classify by sides	all sides equal **Equilateral**	2 sides equal **Isosceles**	no sides equal **Scalene**
Classify by angles	all angles less than 90° **Acute**	one angle of 90° **Right**	one angle greater than 90° **Obtuse**

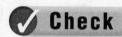 **Check**

1. Match each triangle to its description.

equilateral and acute   isosceles and acute   scalene and right   scalene and obtuse

2. Draw each triangle if you can. If you cannot, explain why.

   a) scalene and obtuse   **b)** obtuse and acute   **c)** equilateral and acute

140

Constructing a Triangle

You can work with geometric tools such as a compass and a protractor to construct a triangle, using given information.

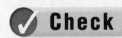

3. Construct a triangle with sides of 4 cm, 3 cm, and 3 cm.
Start by drawing a base 4 cm long.
Label it AB.

a) Hold your compass against a ruler so that the compass point and pencil are 3 cm apart.

b) Put the compass point on A.
Draw an arc.

c) Put the compass point on B.
Draw an arc that crosses the first arc.

d) Mark the point where the arcs intersect.
Label it C.

e) Join A to C. Join B to C.
Measure to check that AC and BC are 3 cm long.
Label each side 3 cm.

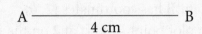

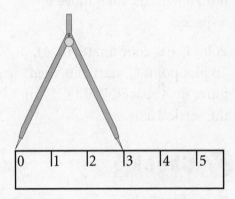

4. Construct ΔEFG with EF = 6 cm, ∠F = 20°, and ∠E = 70°.
Start by drawing EF 6 cm long.

E ————————————————— F

a) Use a protractor to construct a 20° angle at F.

b) Use a protractor to construct a 70° angle at E.

c) Do the arms of these two angles cross?
If they do, label the point where they cross G.
If not, extend the lines to cross.
Label EF = 6 cm, ∠F = 20°, and ∠E = 70°.

KEY TO SUCCESS

- To solve a complex problem, rewrite it in simpler, shorter sentences.
- Write down all of the known information. Use what you know to find out more.

Plotting Points on a Grid

A coordinate grid has a vertical axis and a horizontal axis.

The axes intersect at the origin, O(0, 0).
A point on a grid is described by its coordinates.

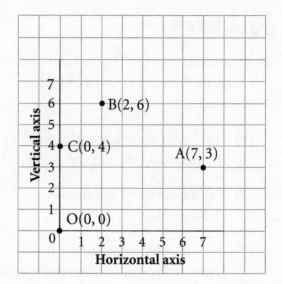

Point A has coordinates (7, 3).
To plot point A, start at 7 on the
horizontal axis, then move up 3
spaces.

Point B has coordinates (2, 6).
To plot point B, start at 2 on the
horizontal axis, then move up
6 spaces.

Point C has coordinates (0, 4).
To plot point C, start at 0, then
move up 4 spaces. Point C is on
the vertical axis.

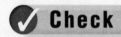 **Check**

5. **a)** Plot A(1, 2).
   Start at 1 on the horizontal axis, then move up 2 spaces.
   Mark and label point A.

   b) Plot B(1, 4).

   Start at _____ on the horizontal axis.

   Move up _____ spaces.
   Mark and label point B.

   c) Plot C(1, 6), D(3, 6), E(3, 4), and F(3, 2).

   d) Connect points A, B, C, D, E, F, and A,
   in this order.
   What figure have you drawn?

   _____

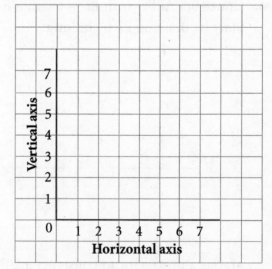

142

Quick Review

➤ A polygon is a closed figure.
   Its sides are line segments that intersect only at the vertices.
   Exactly 2 sides meet at each vertex.

This figure is a polygon.   These figures are not polygons.

➤ A **regular** polygon has all sides and angles equal.
   It also has line symmetry and rotational symmetry.

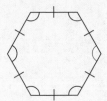

H I N T

Use matching arcs to show equal angles and matching lines to show equal side lengths.

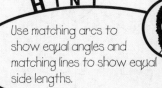

➤ A **convex** polygon has all angles less than 180°.

➤ A **concave** polygon has at least one angle greater than 180°.

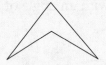

Practice

1. Circle each polygon.

2. Draw all the lines of symmetry through each figure.

3. Match each figure to its description. One is done for you.

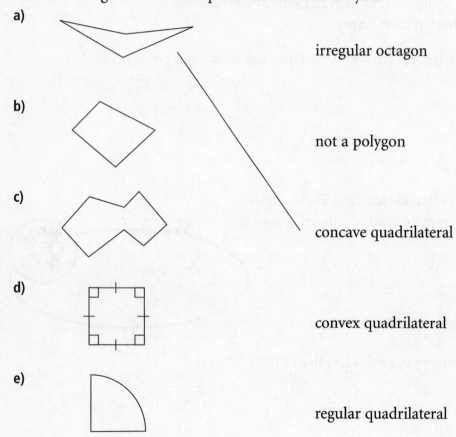

a)

                   irregular octagon

b)

                   not a polygon

c)

                   concave quadrilateral

d)

                   convex quadrilateral

e)

                   regular quadrilateral

4. Draw lines to complete each polygon.

  a) a convex polygon   **b)** a concave polygon   **c)** a pentagon with an angle of 90°

144

5. Draw each polygon.

    a) an equilateral triangle with side
       length 4 units

    b) a parallelogram with side lengths
       3 units and 2 units

    c) a polygon with at least 3 right angles

6. a) Think of a triangle.
    Two of its sides are equal.
    One angle is greater than 90°.

    It is an _____ triangle.

b) Draw the triangle in part a.

    c) Think of a quadrilateral.
    All of its sides are equal.
    It has at least one angle greater
    than 90°.

    It is a _____.

d) Draw the quadrilateral in part c.

145

Quick Review

➤ Congruent figures have the same size and shape.
Triangle ABC is congruent to triangle GHJ.
We write: △ABC ≅ △GHJ

HINT

When you name congruent triangles, list the corresponding vertices in the same order.

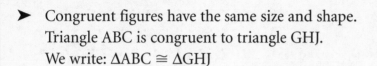

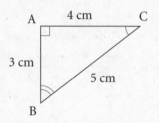

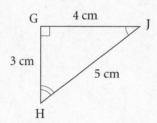

Their corresponding sides are equal.
AB = GH, BC = HJ, AC = GJ

Their corresponding angles are equal.
∠A = ∠G, ∠B = ∠H, ∠C = ∠J

When you know…	You can draw…	Example
all 3 sides	one triangle	△ABC ≅ △DEF
2 sides and 1 angle between them	one triangle	△ABC ≅ △DEF
2 sides and 1 angle not between them	one or more than one triangle	△ABC is not congruent to △DEF.
2 angles and 1 side between them	one triangle	△ABC ≅ △DEF

1. How are these two triangles the same? Different?

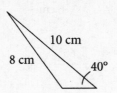 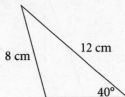

Both triangles have _____

One triangle has _____

The other triangle has _____

2. Name pairs of congruent triangles.
Explain how you know they are congruent.

a)

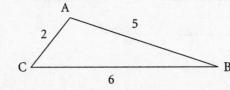

ΔABC ≅ ΔXYZ because: AB   = _____ = 5 units

                        BC   = _____ = _____

                        CA   = _____ = _____

Three pairs of corresponding sides are _____,

so the triangles are _____.

b)

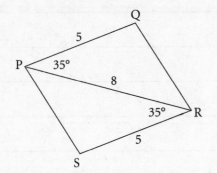

ΔPQR ≅ ΔRSP because:

PQ = _____ = _____

∠QPR = _____ = _____

_____ = _____ = _____

We know that 2 pairs of _____

and 1 pair of _____ between
the sides are equal. So, ΔPQR and ΔRSP are
congruent.

3. Circle the two congruent triangles. Explain your choice.

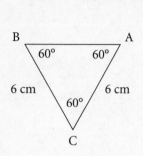 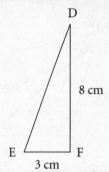 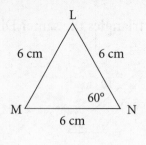 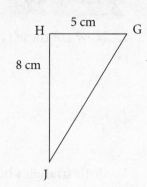

_____

_____

_____

_____

_____

H I N T

 Equilateral triangles have all sides equal and all angles equal.

4. All of these figures have the same side lengths.
Are they all congruent? Explain your answer.

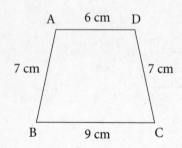 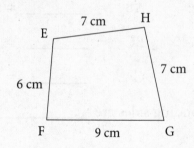 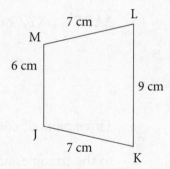

_____

_____

_____

_____

_____

_____

_____

_____

Quick Review

➤ In this **translation**, the shaded figure is moved 4 units right and 1 unit up. The translation image and the shaded figure are congruent.

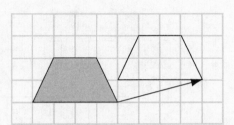

➤ In this **reflection**, the shaded figure is reflected in a vertical line 1 unit to the right of the figure. The reflection image and the shaded figure are congruent.

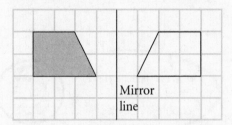

Mirror line

➤ In this **rotation**, the shaded figure is rotated a $\frac{3}{4}$ turn clockwise about a turn centre.

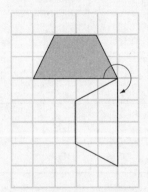

You get the same image if you rotate the shaded figure a $\frac{1}{4}$ turn counterclockwise.

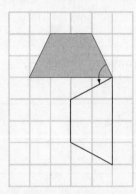

In this case, the turn centre is the bottom right corner of the figure. The rotation image and the shaded figure are congruent.

Practice

1. Match each illustration to the transformation it shows.

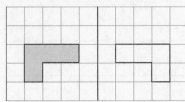   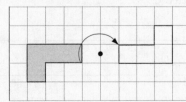   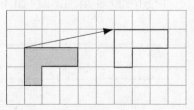

translation   reflection   rotation

149

2. What transformation is described in each case?

   a) You ride your bicycle along a straight road. _____

   b) You turn the pedals on your bicycle. _____

   c) The hands on your wristwatch move around the dial. _____

   d) You walk to school. _____

   e) You look in a mirror. _____

3. Identify each transformation.

HINT

You can rotate a figure clockwise or counterclockwise.

   a) Figure B is the image of Figure A.

   _____

   _____

   _____

   _____

   b) Figure C is the image of Figure B.

   _____

   _____

   c) Figure D is the image of Figure C.

   _____

   _____

4. a) Translate Figure A 3 units left and 4 units up.

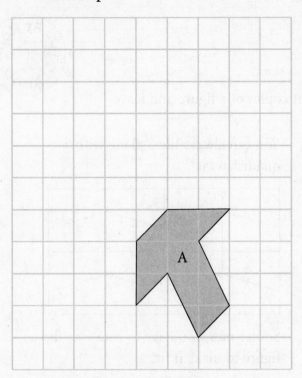

b) Reflect Figure A in the horizontal line one unit below it.

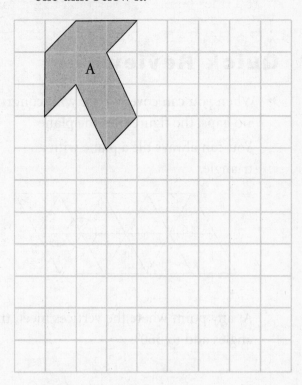

c) Rotate Figure A a $\frac{1}{2}$ turn clockwise about the bottom corner.

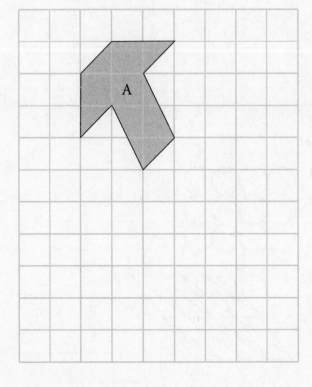

d) Rotate Figure A a $\frac{1}{4}$ turn counterclockwise about the bottom corner.

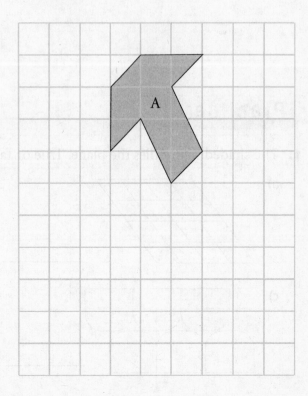

Quick Review

➤ When you can cover a page with congruent copies of a figure and leave no gaps, the figure **tiles the plane**.

You can always tile a plane with a triangle.

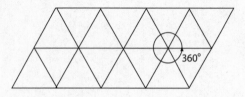

At any point where the vertices meet, the angles add to 360°.

You can always tile a plane with a quadrilateral.

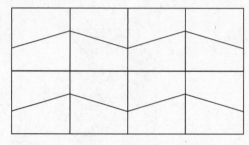

Sometimes, you have to rotate or flip a figure to make it fit.

➤ There are some figures, like this heptagon, that will not tile the plane because they leave gaps.

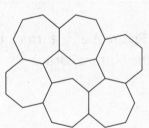

Practice

1. The shaded figure tiles the plane. True or false?

a)

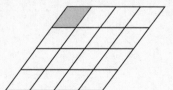

_____

b)

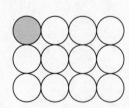

_____

c)

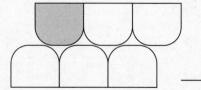

_____

d)

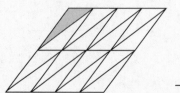

_____

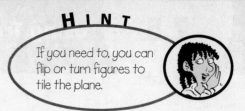

H I N T

If you need to, you can
flip or turn figures to
tile the plane.

2. Circle the figures that will tile the plane.
Explain why you chose each figure.

 A   B   C   D   E   F

_____

_____

3. The shaded figure tiles the plane. True or false?
Use a drawing to support your answer.

a)

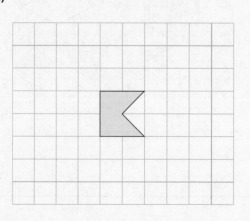

_____

b)

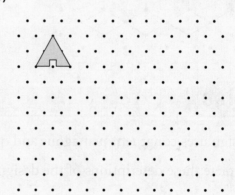

_____

c)

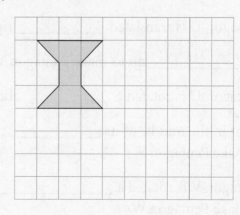

_____

d)

_____

153

Quick Review

➤ Some figures tile the plane by themselves.
Sometimes you may need more than one type of congruent figure to cover a surface.
These two figures, when used together, tile the plane.

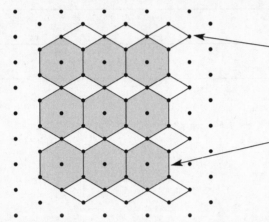

The rhombuses are all **translated** images of each other.

The hexagons are all **translated** images of each other.

Practice

1. This design uses congruent pentagons and quadrilaterals.

    a) Complete these descriptions of the design.

    Pentagon U is reflected in a _____ line

    along its _____ side to make
    Pentagon V.

    Pentagon U is translated _____ right

    and _____ up to make Pentagon W.

    Pentagon U is rotated a _____ about a

    point in the middle of its _____
    to make Pentagon V.

    Pentagon V is rotated a _____
    to make Pentagon W.

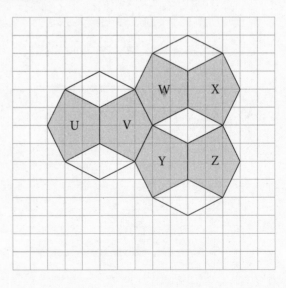

    b) Continue the design under Pentagons U and V.

154

2. a) Continue this pattern to cover the grid.

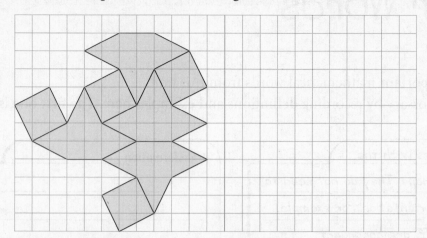

b) Use transformations to describe the design.

The square is translated _____ right and _____ up.

The same square is translated _____ right and _____ down.

The heptagon is reflected in _____.

Both the figure and the image are translated _____ right and _____ up.

The same 2 figures are translated _____ right and _____ down.

3. a) Make a design using 2 or more figures that together tile the plane.
Start with a quadrilateral of your choice.
Use congruent copies of your figures.

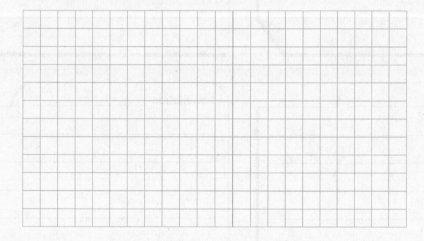

b) Use transformations to describe your design.

_____

_____

_____

In Your Words

Here are some important mathematical words from this unit.
Build your own glossary by recording definitions and examples here. The first one is done for you.

congruent _Figures with the same size and shape. They do not need to have the same orientation. For example, $\triangle ABC$ and $\triangle DFE$ are congruent._

transformation _____

convex polygon _____

tiling the plane _____

concave polygon _____

tessellation _____

List other mathematical words you need to know.

_____

Unit Review

LESSON

7.1   **1.** Circle each polygon. Explain why you chose each figure.

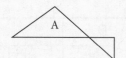 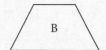

_____

2. Match each polygon to its description.

a)   a pentagon with an angle of 120°

b)   an irregular polygon with no lines of symmetry

c)   a kite with one right angle

d)   a regular polygon with 6 sides

120°

7.2   **3.** Find pairs of congruent triangles. Explain why they are congruent.

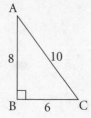 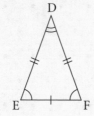 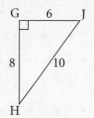 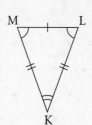

_____

_____

_____

7.3 **4.** Identify each transformation.

  a) Figure B is the image of Figure A.

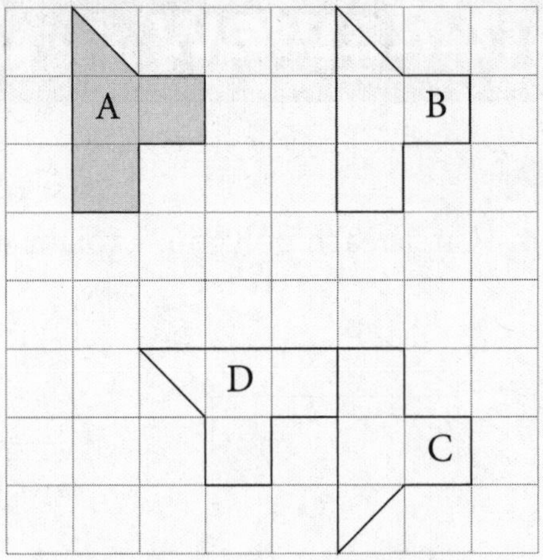

  _____

  _____

  b) Figure C is the image of Figure B.

  _____

  _____

  c) Figure D is the image of Figure C.

  _____

  _____

7.4 **5.** Circle the figures that will tile the plane. Explain why you chose each figure.

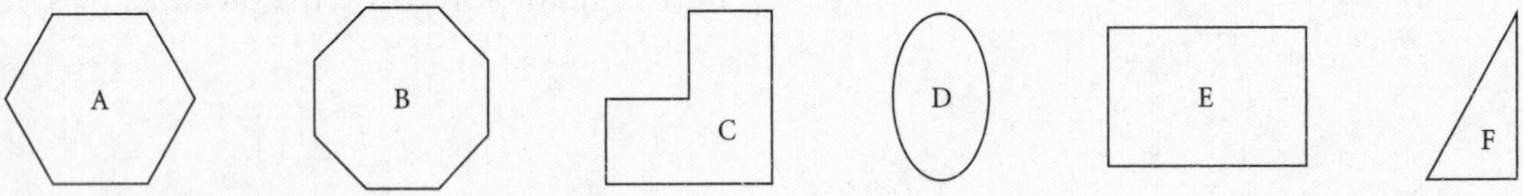

_____

_____

_____

_____

7.5 **6.** Use translations and reflections of the hexagon and triangle to tile the dot paper.

Working with Percents

Just for Fun

Toothpick Shapes

Use 16 toothpicks to build this design.

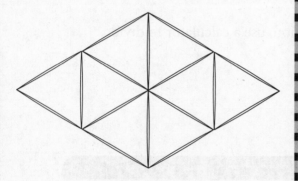

How can you take away 4 toothpicks to leave exactly 4 equilateral triangles?

Penny Turnover

Place 4 pennies on the table, tails up.

A move consists of turning any 3 coins over. What is the least number of moves that will show 4 heads? Explain. Remember, you must turn over 3 coins each time!

_____

_____

Pick Up

A Game for 2

You will need 13 counters.

Make 2 piles of counters.
One pile should have 7 counters and the other pile should have 6 counters.
You and your partner can take turns picking up counters.

You may:
• take as many counters as you want from one pile, or
• take the same number of counters from both piles

The player who picks up the last counter wins.
What can Player 1 do so she will always win?

_____

_____

Skills You'll Need

Writing a Fraction As a Decimal

➤ You can write a fraction as a decimal by writing an equivalent fraction with denominator 100.

$\frac{3}{4} \overset{\times 25}{\underset{\times 25}{=}} \frac{75}{100}$

$\frac{75}{100} = 0.75$

So, $\frac{3}{4} = 0.75$

➤ When you cannot write an equivalent fraction, use a calculator to divide.

$\frac{3}{8}$ means $3 \div 8$.

Key in: 3 $\boxed{\div}$ 8 $\boxed{=}$ to display 0.375

$\frac{3}{8} = 0.375$

Example 1

Write each fraction as a decimal.

a) $\frac{2}{5}$

b) $\frac{9}{16}$

Solution

a) 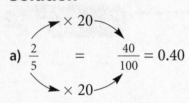 $\frac{2}{5} \overset{\times 20}{\underset{\times 20}{=}} \frac{40}{100} = 0.40$

b) Use a calculator.

Key in: 9 $\boxed{\div}$ 16 $\boxed{=}$

$\frac{9}{16} = 0.5625$

✔ Check

1. Write each fraction as a decimal by writing an equivalent fraction with denominator 100.

a) $\frac{3}{20} =$ _____

   $=$ _____

b) $\frac{4}{5} =$ _____

   $=$ _____

c) $\frac{1}{2} =$ _____

   $=$ _____

d) $\frac{4}{25} =$ _____

   $=$ _____

2. Write each fraction as a decimal. Use a calculator if necessary.

a) $\frac{1}{8} =$ _____

b) $\frac{1}{16} =$ _____

c) $\frac{7}{8} =$ _____

d) $\frac{5}{16} =$ _____

Percent

Percent means "per hundred" or "out of 100."
One whole, or 1, is 100%.

So: 25% is $\frac{25}{100}$ 4% is $\frac{4}{100}$ 100% is $\frac{100}{100}$ or 1

Example 2

This is a hundredths grid.

a) What percent of the hundredths grid is shaded?
b) What percent of the hundredths grid is not shaded?

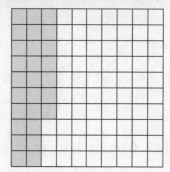

Solution

a) 27 out of 100 squares are shaded.

$$\frac{27}{100} = 27\%$$

27% of the grid is shaded.

b) 73 out of 100 squares are not shaded.

$$\frac{73}{100} = 73\%$$

73% of the grid is not shaded.

✓ **Check**

3. Write a fraction with denominator 100 for the shaded part of each hundredths grid. Then write each fraction as a percent.

a)

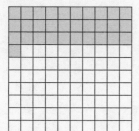

_____ = _____

b)

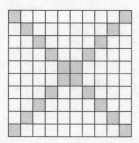

_____ = _____

Quick Review

You can describe part of a whole in 3 ways:
- as a fraction
- as a decimal
- as a percent

The hundredths grid has $\frac{3}{4}$ of the squares shaded.

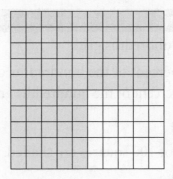

➤ To write a fraction as a percent, first write the
fraction with denominator 100.
75 out of 100 squares are shaded.
So, $\frac{3}{4}$ = 75%
Since percent means per hundred, $\frac{75}{100}$ = 75%
If you divide 75 by 100, $\frac{75}{100}$ = 0.75
So, 75% = 0.75

$$\frac{3}{4} = \frac{75}{100}$$
× 25
× 25

➤ When you cannot write the fraction with denominator 100,
use a calculator to divide.
$\frac{3}{8}$ = 0.375

$= \frac{375}{1000}$

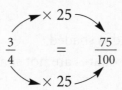

$$\frac{375}{1000} = \frac{37.5}{100} = 37.5\%$$
÷ 10
÷ 10

Practice

1. Describe the shaded part of each hundredths grid.
   Use a fraction, a decimal, and a percent.

   a)
   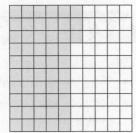

   b)
   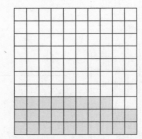

   $\dfrac{}{100} = 0.\underline{} = \underline{}$ %

   $\underline{} = \underline{} = \underline{}$

2. Write each fraction as a percent. Use a calculator if necessary.

a) $\dfrac{3}{10}$ = _____

b) $\dfrac{9}{10}$ = _____

c) $\dfrac{9}{50}$ = _____

d) $\dfrac{7}{20}$ = _____

e) $\dfrac{17}{20}$ = _____

f) $\dfrac{4}{5}$ = _____

g) $\dfrac{3}{2}$ = _____

h) $\dfrac{5}{4}$ = _____

i) $\dfrac{7}{5}$ = _____

j) $\dfrac{5}{8}$ = _____

k) $\dfrac{3}{16}$ = _____

l) $\dfrac{7}{8}$ = _____

3. Bennett had 19 out of 20 on a spelling test.
Write Bennett's mark as a percent.

_____

4. In Ms. Khan's class, 22 out of 25 students hand in their projects on time.
What percent of the class hand in their projects on time?

_____

5. Use 4 different colours to shade the squares on this hundredths grid as given in the table.
Describe each coloured part as a fraction, a decimal, and a percent.

Colour	Fraction	Decimal	Percent
Red	$\dfrac{6}{25}$		
Yellow			35%
Green		0.20	
Purple			18%
White			

R = red, Y = yellow, P = purple, G = green, W = white

6. Describe the shaded part of each diagram.
Use a fraction, a decimal, and a percent.

a)

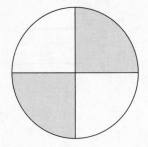

b)

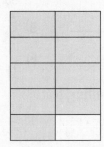

c)

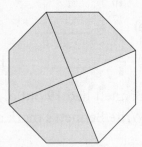

_____   _____   _____

7. Lucy and Victor are sharing pens.
Lucy has $\frac{1}{4}$ of the pens, and Victor has 20% of the pens.
Who has more pens? Explain.

Since _____ % > _____ %, _____

8. Raymond surveyed 10 classmates to find out which shoe, left or right,
each person puts on first.
His results are shown in this table.

Left Shoe First	Right Shoe First
卌 l	llll

a) What percent of the students surveyed put on their left shoe first?

_____

b) What percent of the students surveyed put on their right shoe first?

_____

9. The *Fashion Depot* is having a big sale this week.
Everything is $\frac{1}{5}$ off the regular price.
What percent of the full price do you pay? Explain.

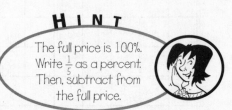

H I N T
The full price is 100%.
Write $\frac{1}{5}$ as a percent.
Then, subtract from
the full price.

_____

Quick Review

You can use mental math to estimate and calculate percent.

➤ Thirteen out of 19 students sign up for basketball.
Estimate the percent of students who sign up for basketball.

$$\frac{13}{19} \doteq \frac{13}{20} \longleftarrow \text{Change } \frac{13}{19} \text{ to a "friendly" fraction.}$$

$$\frac{13}{20} \overset{\times 5}{\underset{\times 5}{=}} \frac{65}{100} = 65\%$$

Approximately 65% of the students sign up for basketball.

➤ Estimate 30% of $64.97.

Round $64.97 to $65.00.
To find 30% of $65, find 10% of $65.00.
Then multiply your answer by 3.

10% of $65.00 = 0.1 × $65.00 = $6.50
$6.50 × 3 = $19.50
So, 30% of $64.97 is about $19.50.

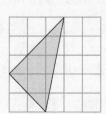

30%
off all sporting goods!

Practice

1. Estimate the percent of each grid that is shaded.

a)
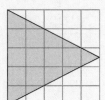

b)
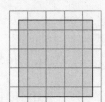

c)
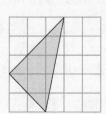

_____   _____   _____

2. Estimate each percent.
Approximate each fraction to a friendly fraction to help you.

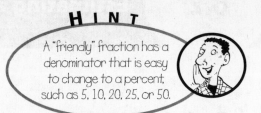

a) 12 out of 27

$\frac{12}{27} \doteq \frac{12}{25}$

$\frac{12}{25} = \frac{}{100} = \underline{\hspace{1cm}}$ %

b) 7 out of 9

$\frac{7}{9} \doteq \underline{\hspace{1.5cm}}$

$\underline{\hspace{1cm}} = \underline{\hspace{1cm}} = \underline{\hspace{1cm}}$

c) 30 out of 21

$\underline{\hspace{1cm}} \doteq \underline{\hspace{1cm}}$

$\underline{\hspace{1cm}} = \underline{\hspace{1cm}} = \underline{\hspace{1cm}}$

3. Find 10% of each number.

a) 60

10% of 60 = 0.1 × 60 = _____

b) 85

10% of 85 = _____ × _____ = _____

c) 150

_____

d) 55

_____

4. Find 30% of each number in question 3.

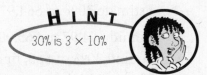

a) 3 × _____ = _____

30% of 60 = _____

b) 3 × _____ = _____

30% of 85 = _____

c) _____

30% of 150 = _____

d) _____

30% of 55 = _____

5. Estimate.

a) 25% of 78

Round 78 to 80.

25% of 80 = 0.25 × 80 = _____

25% of 78 is about _____.

b) 49% of 90

Round 49% to _____ %.

_____ % of 90 = _____ × 90 = _____

49% of 90 is about _____.

c) 15% of $7.90

_____

_____

_____

d) 131% of 60

_____

_____

6. Asher's new backpack costs $29.95 plus 15% sales tax.
Estimate how much Asher pays in total for the backpack.
Show your work.

So, Asher pays about $ _____ for the backpack.

7. Imelda's jigsaw puzzle has 500 pieces.
She estimates that she has put together approximately 95 of the pieces.

a) About what percent of the puzzle has Imelda put together?

Imelda has put together about _____ of the puzzle.

b) About what percent of the puzzle does Imelda still have to put together?

Imelda still has to put together about _____ of the puzzle.

8. Here is a diagram of Sanjay's patio.
What percent of the patio does the hot tub take up?
Show your work.

The hot tub takes up about _____ of Sanjay's patio.

Quick Review

A scooter originally cost $89.98.
It is on sale at 45% off.
To find how much you save on the scooter,
find 45% of $89.98.

$45\% = \dfrac{45}{100} = 0.45$

HINT
To calculate a percent of a number, write the percent as a decimal.

So, 45% of $89.98 = 0.45 × $89.98
To multiply 0.45 × $89.98,
multiply without the decimal points.

```
      8 9 9 8
  ×       4 5
    4 4 9 9 0
  3 5 9 9 2 0
  4 0.4 9 1 0
```

Estimate: 45% is close to 50%, or $\dfrac{1}{2}$.
$89.98 is about $90.00.
$\dfrac{1}{2}$ of $90.00 is $45.00.

So, 0.45 × 89.98 = 40.491
Round to 2 decimal places: 40.491 ≐ 40.49
So, 45% of $89.98 ≐ $40.49
You save about $40.49 on the scooter.

HINT
Estimate to place the decimal point in the answer. There are 4 decimal places in the question. There should be 4 decimal places in the answer.

Practice

1. Find each percent.

a) 7% of 80

$7\% = \dfrac{7}{100} =$ _____

_____ × 80 = _____

b) 1% of 25.5

_____

_____

 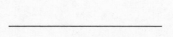

Tip
The word "of" tells you to multiply.

c) 20% of 60.5

_____

_____

d) 110% of 50

_____

_____

168

2. Find each percent. Show your work.

a) 25% of 65

b) 37% of 182

c) 150% of 74

_____ _____ _____

_____ _____ _____

3. Marco's dinner bill is $14.80. He leaves the server a 15% tip.
How much does Marco pay for his dinner, including the tip? Show your work.

So, Marco paid _____ for his dinner.

4. There are 620 students at Irena's school.
Of these students, 45% have attended at least one other school.

a) How many students have attended more than 1 school?

So, _____ students have attended more than 1 school.

b) How many students have attended just 1 school?

So, _____ students have attended just 1 school.

5. Hraa has 120 baseball cards. She gives 25% of them away.
How many cards does Hraa have left?

Hraa has _____ cards left.

6. Which would you rather have? Explain.
90% of $70 or 15% of $500

Quick Review

A class of 25 students takes a test.
This table shows their grades.

Test Results	
Grade	**Number of Students**
A	5
B	15
C	3
D	2

To draw a circle graph to display the data, follow these steps.

➤ Write each number as a fraction of 25, then as a percent.

A: $\frac{5}{25} = \frac{20}{100} = 0.20 = 20\%$ B: $\frac{15}{25} = \frac{60}{100} = 0.60 = 60\%$

C: $\frac{3}{25} = \frac{12}{100} = 0.12 = 12\%$ D: $\frac{2}{25} = \frac{8}{100} = 0.08 = 8\%$

➤ A circle has a central angle of 360°.
Multiply each decimal by 360° to find the sector angle for each grade.
Round to the nearest degree, if necessary.

A: $0.20 \times 360° = 72°$

B: $0.60 \times 360° = 216°$

C: $0.12 \times 360° = 43.2° \doteq 43°$

D: $0.08 \times 360° = 28.8° \doteq 29°$

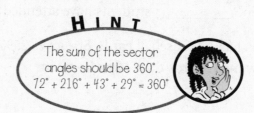

HINT

The sum of the sector
angles should be 360°.
$72° + 216° + 43° + 29° = 360°$

➤ Draw a circle. Measure the sector angle
for each grade with a protractor.
Label each sector with a grade and a percent.
Write a title for the circle graph.

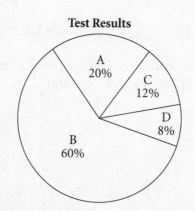

Test Results

A 20%
C 12%
D 8%
B 60%

Practice

1. In a survey, 500 senior citizens are asked,
   "What is your favourite form of exercise?"
   The results are shown in the circle graph.
   How many senior citizens chose each form of exercise?

   Favourite Form of Exercise

   a) Walking 50%: 0._____ × _____ = _____

   b) Tai Chi 27%: _____

   c) Swimming _____

   d) Treadmill _____

2. Carl earns $200 babysitting.
   This table shows how he spends
   his earnings.

Item	Amount Spent
Clothing	$100.00
Books	$30.00
Sports equipment	$50.00
Movies	$20.00

   a) Find each percent.

   Clothing: $\frac{100}{200} = \frac{50}{100} = 0.50 =$ _____ %

   Books: _____

   Sports equipment: _____

   Movies: _____

   H I N T

   Write each amount as a
   fraction of 200. Then write
   an equivalent fraction with
   denominator 100.

   b) Find the sector angle for each item.

   Clothing: 0.50 × 360° = _____

   Books: _____

   Sports equipment: _____

   Movies: _____

   c) Draw a circle graph to display the data.

   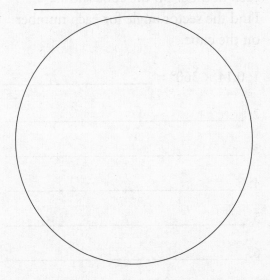

3. Indonesia has an area of approximately 2 000 000 km². This circle graph shows how the land is divided. Find the area of each. Explain.

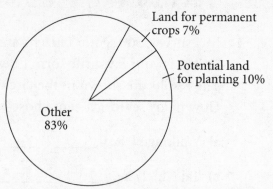

Land Type in Indonesia

Land for permanent crops 7%

Potential land for planting 10%

Other 83%

a) Potential land for planting: _____

   10% of 2 000 000 = 0.10 × 2 000 000 = _____

b) Land for permanent crops: _____

c) Land for other purposes: _____

4. Phoebe rolls a number cube labelled 1 to 6 50 times. The tally chart shows how many times each number on the cube is shown.

a) Find the percent of times each number is shown.

   1: $\frac{7}{50} = \frac{14}{100} = 0.14 =$ _____ %

   2: _____

   3: _____

   4: _____

   5: _____

   6: _____

Number	Frequency
1	ⅢⅡ
2	ⅢⅢ
3	Ⅲ Ⅰ
4	ⅢⅢ ⅢⅢ ⅢⅢ
5	ⅢⅢ ⅢⅢ
6	ⅢⅢ

b) A circle is drawn to show how often each number on the cube shows. Find the sector angle for each number on the cube.

   1: 0.14 × 360° = _____

   2: _____

   3: _____

   4: _____

   5: _____

   6: _____

c) Draw a circle graph to show the data.

   _____

172

Quick Review

➤ If you know the percent and the value of the percent, then you can find 100%.

360 students participate in the walk-a-thon.
This is 75% of the school population.
To find how many students attend the school, you find 100%.

We know 75% of the school population is 360 students.

So, 1% is: $\frac{360}{75}$

Divide: $360 \div 75 = 4.8$

$$\begin{array}{r} 4.8 \\ 75 \overline{)360.0} \\ \underline{300} \\ 600 \\ \underline{600} \\ 0 \end{array}$$

HINT

Use a calculator to divide "less friendly" numbers.

1% is 4.8.

100% is: $4.8 \times 100 = 480$

So, 480 students attend the school.

Practice

1. Divide to find 100%.

a) 10% is 45 cm.

   1% is: $\frac{45}{10}$ cm = _____

   100% is: _____ $\times$ 100 = _____

b) 37% is $29.60.

   1% is: _____

   100% is: _____

c) 75% is 18.6 m.

   1% is: _____

   100% is: _____

d) 30% is 9.9 cm.

   1% is: _____

   100% is: _____

2. a) Suppose 18 is 48%. What is 100%?

_____

_____

b) Suppose 170 is 25%. What is 100%?

_____

_____

c) Suppose 175% of a number is 28. What is 100%?

_____

_____

d) Suppose 24 is 2%. What is 100%?

_____

_____

e) Suppose 398 is 125%. What is 100%?

_____

_____

Tip

100% is the original number.

3. In a survey, people were asked if they plan to buy a new computer this year.
Of those who were surveyed, 32%, or 128 people, said "yes."
How many people were surveyed?

So, _____ people were surveyed.

4. There are 15 vacant units in Noor's apartment building.
This represents 6% of the total number of units.
How many units are in Noor's apartment building?

There are _____ units in Noor's building.

5. A hockey stick is on sale for 25% off.
The sale price of the hockey stick is $16.50.
What is the original price of the hockey stick?

HINT
Think: what percent of the original price is $16.50?

The original price is _____.

6. The area of Nunavut is 2 093 190 km^2.
This area represents about 21% of the total area of Canada.
What is the approximate area of Canada?
Round your answer to the nearest 1000 km^2.

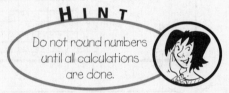

HINT
Do not round numbers until all calculations are done.

The area of Canada is about _____.

7. The sales tax in Ontario is 15%.
Janis pays a total of $33.35 for a fishing pole.
Find the cost of the fishing pole before sales tax.

HINT
The cost is 100%.

8. A sweater is on sale for 20% off.
A jacket is on sale for 15% off.
The sale price for each item is $34.00.
Which item cost more originally? By how much?

In Your Words

Here are some of the important mathematical words of this unit.
Build your own glossary by recording definitions and examples here. The first one is done for you.

percent _a way to express_
per hundred, or out of 100
For example, 25% of this square is shaded.

fraction _____

decimal _____

one hundred percent _____

friendly fraction _____

circle graph _____

List other mathematical words you need to know.

_____

Unit Review

LESSON

8.1 **1.** Write each fraction with denominator 100, then as a decimal, and then as a percent.

a) $\frac{7}{10}$ = _____

b) $\frac{3}{4}$ = _____

c) $\frac{9}{25}$ = _____

d) $\frac{13}{10}$ = _____

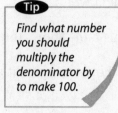

Tip

Find what number you should multiply the denominator by to make 100.

2. Write each fraction as a decimal and a percent.

a) $\frac{5}{8}$ = _____

b) $\frac{3}{24}$ = _____

c) $\frac{9}{75}$ = _____

d) $\frac{9}{8}$ = _____

3. Ivana got $\frac{21}{25}$ on her science test.

She got 86% on her math test.

Which of her test marks is better? Explain.

So, Ivana did better on the _____ test.

8.2 **4.** Estimate.

a) 24% of 200   b) 51% of 128   c) 5% of 41

_____   _____   _____

8.3 **5.** Find each percent.

a) 3% of 25   b) 24% of $9.00   c) 140% of 95

$3\% = \frac{3}{100} = 0.03$ 24% = _____   _____

0.03×25 = _____   _____   _____

6. Sylvia is going to buy a new jacket.
The regular price is $68.00 and
the jacket is on sale for 25% off.
There is 15% sales tax on the jacket.
How much will Sylvia pay for the jacket?

Sylvia will pay _____ for the jacket.

8.4   **7.** This table shows the favourite types of books of 50 grade 7 students.

    a) Find the percent of students who chose each type of book.

Suspense: _____

Science fiction: _____

Biography: _____

Romance: _____

Type of Book	Number of Students
Suspense	24
Science fiction	14
Biography	3
Romance	9

    b) Draw a circle graph to display the data.

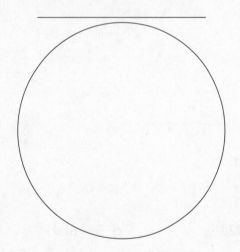

_____

> **Tip**
> Calculate the sector angle for each percent by multiplying by 360°.

8.5   **8.** Lucas plants 20% of his garden with cucumber plants.
The cucumber plants cover an area of 24 m².
What is the total area of Lucas's garden?

Just for Fun

Magic Square

In this magic square, each row, column, and diagonal has a sum of 15.
Use each number from 1 to 9 once.
Complete the magic square.

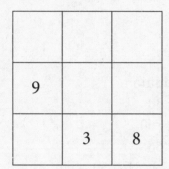

The Square Route

Go from Start to Finish by adding and subtracting.
Do not pass through the same point twice.
Which route has the greatest total?

What is the total? _____

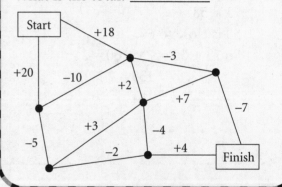

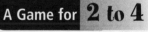

The Three Towers

Use counters or coins to build three towers: one of 8, one of 9, and one of 10.

On a turn, a player can either
- take 1 counter from each tower, or
- take 2 counters from one tower

Score 1 point for every counter you collect.
Score 5 points every time you take the last counter from a tower.

Continue until the towers are gone.
If you have the most points, you win!

Variation: Use towers of different heights or a different number of towers.

Skills You'll Need

Mental Math Strategies for Addition and Subtraction

There are many ways to add or subtract mentally.

- Look for 10s, or the nearest 10.
- Make a friendly number.
- Add in a different order.
- Subtract by "adding on."

Example

Add or subtract. Use mental math.

a) $73 + 58$

b) $66 - 29$

Solution

a) $73 + 58$
   58 is close to 60.
   So $73 + 58 = 73 + 60 - 2$
   $ = 133 - 2$
   $ = 131$

b) $66 - 29$
   Think addition.
   $29 + 1 = 30$
   $30 + 30 = 60$
   $60 + 6 = 66$
   So, $66 - 29 = 1 + 30 + 6$
   $ = 37$

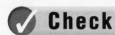 **Check**

1. Add or subtract. What mental math strategy did you use?

   a) $152 - 84 =$ _____

   _____

   _____

   b) $68 + 36 =$ _____

   _____

   _____

   c) $218 - 153 =$ _____

   _____

Quick Review

➤ A **positive number** is greater than 0.
A **negative number** is less than 0.
0 is neither positive nor negative.

➤ The **integers** are the numbers
... –3, –2, –1, 0, +1, +2, +3, ...

You can show integers on a number line.

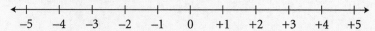

➤ **Opposite integers** are the same distance from 0 on a number line
but are on opposite sides of 0.

For example, –3 and +3 are opposite integers.

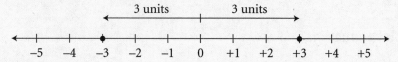

Practice

1. The long-term forecast gives these temperatures for the next 5 days.
On the thermometer, show each day's predicted high temperature.

Mon	Tues	Wed	Thur	Fri
High +8 Low +2	High +6 Low 0	High 0 Low –4	High –3 Low –7	High –5 Low –10

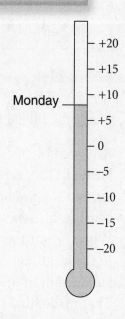

2. Mark each integer on the number line.

a) +2   b) –7   c) +8   d) –3

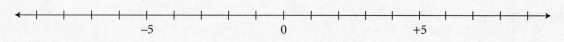

181

3. Write the opposite of each integer.
Show the first 3 pairs of opposite integers on the number line.

a) +1: _____

b) −5: _____

c) −7: _____

d) +20: _____

e) −501: _____

f) +99: _____

←—+—+—+—+—+—+—+—+—+—+—+—+—+—+—+—+—+—+—→
                              0

4. Use a positive or negative integer to represent each situation.

a) losing $15: _____

b) throwing a ball 9 m straight up: _____

c) seventeen days from now: _____

d) a submarine 830 m below the water's surface: _____

5. Use each integer to describe a situation.

a) +5000: _____

_____

b) −5: _____

_____

6. Circle the integers that match descriptions in this story.

Pat owed his sister $24.
He had $108 in his bank account.
So, he took the bus to the bank.
The bus fare was $2.
When he got there, he took the elevator up 3 floors
to the customer service section.
He was 5th in line, so he had to wait.
That made him 15 min late for soccer practice.
He had to run 5 penalty laps.
What a day!

−1

+3

+108

−15   −108

+15   +5   −24

−5

−3

+2   −2

−7

+24

Quick Review

➤ You can use a number line to compare integers.

Compare +2 and −3.

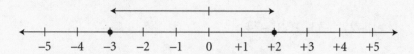

+2 is to the right of −3 on a number line.
+2 is greater than −3, so you write: +2 > −3
−3 is less than +2, so you write: −3 < +2
−3 < +2 or +2 > −3

➤ To order integers from least to greatest,
write them as they appear from left to right on a number line.

➤ To order integers from greatest to least,
write them as they appear from right to left on a number line.

Order +2, −3, 0, and +5 from least to greatest.

From left to right, or from least to greatest: −3, 0, +2, +5

Practice

1. Fill in the missing integers.

2. Place either > or < between the integers.
Use a number line if it helps.

a) +9 _____ 0

b) +7 _____ +2

c) +4 _____ +8

d) −10 _____ −1

e) −2 _____ +10

f) +2 _____ −10

3. Circle the least integer in each set.

a) +12, +3, +8

b) 0, +5, −7

c) −8, +8, −9, +9

d) +6, −4, +2, 0

e) −10, −3, +3, 0

f) −5, +10, −20, +40

4. Order the integers in each set from least to greatest.

a) 0, +8, −8

b) −5, +2, −9

c) −20, +1, −1

_____

_____

_____

d) +5, −1, +1, −5

e) −27, −33, +30, −24

f) −5, +6, −7, +8

_____

_____

_____

5. Order the integers in each set from greatest to least.

a) +2, +4, −3

b) −3, +1, −4

c) +2, −7, −18

_____

_____

_____

d) +1, −1, +2, −2

e) +16, −4, +6, 0

f) 0, +20, −50, −60

_____

_____

_____

6. Martina ran a floor hockey tournament.
She calculated a team's point difference by subtracting their goals against
from their goals scored.

Team Name	Point Difference
The Athletes	−2
The Blasters	+9
The Champions	−18
The Dolphins	+18
The Eagles	+7
The Firebolts	−14

a) Mark each point difference on the number line.

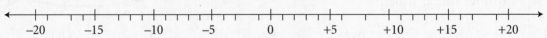

b) Which team had the lowest point difference?

_____

184

Quick Review

➤ You can use tiles to represent integers.

| + | | − | | + − | = 0 |

represents +1.   represents −1.   This is a zero pair.

Here are 3 ways to model −3.

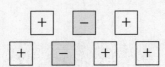

• − − −

• [+ on −] [+ on −] − ... (set models −3)

• Each set models −3.

➤ Write the integer modelled by these tiles.

+ − +
+ − + +

Arrange the tiles in rows.

Circle the zero pairs.

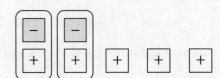

There are 3 | + | tiles left. They model +3.

185

Practice

1. Write the integer modelled by each set of tiles.

a) _____ `+` `+` `+` `+`

b) _____ `−` `−` `−` `−` `−`

H I N T

Circle the zero pairs and count the remaining tiles.

c) _____ `+` `+` `+`
   `−` `−`

d) _____ `+`
   `−` `−` `−` `−`

e) _____ `+` `+` `+`
   `−` `−` `−` `−`

f) _____ `+` `+` `+` `+` `+` `+`
   `−`

2. Draw tiles to model each integer.

a) +2

b) +5

c) −1

d) −3

e) +8

f) −7

3. Use tiles representing +1 and tiles representing −1.
Draw tiles to model +2 two more ways.

`+` `+` `+` `+`
`−` `−`

4. Explain why you cannot model +2 using three tiles.

_____

_____

_____

_____

Quick Review

You can add integers by modelling with tiles.

- Add: (−2) + (−4)

  −2: [−] [−]

  −4: [−] [−] [−] [−]

  } There are 6 [−] tiles.
  They model −6.

  So, (−2) + (−4) = −6

- Add (+3) + (−4) + (+3).

  +3: [+] [+] [+]

  −4: [−] [−] [−] [−]

  +3: [+] [+] [+]

  Circle the zero pairs. Count the tiles that are left.

  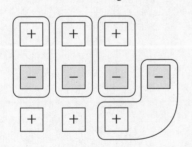

  } There are 4 zero pairs.
  There are 2 [+] tiles left.
  They model +2.

  So, (+3) + (−4) + (+3) = +2

Practice

1. Use tiles representing +1 and tiles representing −1 to add. (+4) + (−6)

   a) Circle zero pairs.

   b) What tiles are left? _____

   c) So, (+4) + (−6) = _____

187

2. Use tiles to add. $(-2) + (-5) + (+3)$

   a) Circle zero pairs.

   b) What tiles are left? _____

   c) So, $(-2) + (-5) + (+3) =$ _____

3. What sum does each set of tiles model? Find each sum.

a)

       $(+1) + (+3) =$ _____

b)

       $(-3) +$ _____ $=$ _____

c)

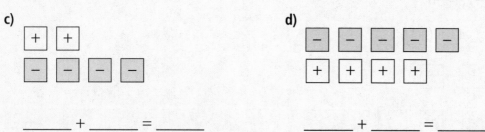

     _____ $+$ _____ $=$ _____

d)

     _____ $+$ _____ $=$ _____

4. Draw tiles to represent each sum. Complete the addition equation.

   a) $(+3) + (+4) =$ _____

   b) $(-2) + (+5) =$ _____

   c) $(-7) + (+2) =$ _____

   d) $(-3) + (+4) + (-2) =$ _____

5. A mine elevator was at level -5 (5 levels below ground).
It went up 3 levels.
What level is it at now? _____

HINT

Think: Shall I represent a rise in the elevator position by a positive integer or a negative integer?

Quick Review

➤ You can add integers using a number line.

To add a positive integer, move right.
To add a negative integer, move left.

Add. (−7) + (+13)
Start at −7.
This is 7 units to the left of 0.

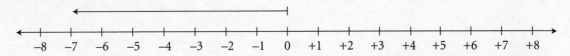

H I N T

Always start the second arrow where the first arrow ended.

Then, add +13.
Move 13 units to the right.

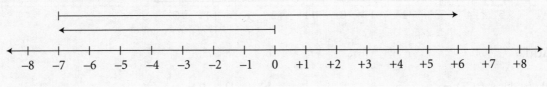

(−7) + (+13) = +6

Practice

1. Use the number line to add. (+3) + (−7)

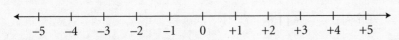

a) Start at 0. Move 3 units right.

b) Move _____ units left.

c) (+3) + (−7) = _____

KEY TO SUCCESS

If you know different methods, you can solve a problem in one way, and check the answer in another way.

189

2. Use the number line to add.

a) (+4) + (−5) = _____

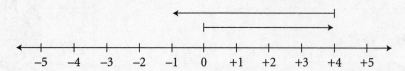

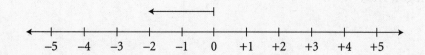

b) (−2) + (−2) = _____

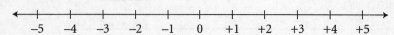

c) (−4) + (+8) = _____

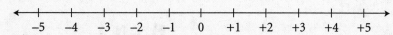

d) (−1) + (+2) + (−4) = _____

HINT

To add positive integers, move right. To add negative integers, move left.

3. Add.

a) (+4) + (+7) = _____

b) (−2) + 0 = _____

c) (+9) + (−5) = _____

d) (−10) + (+3) + (+7) = _____

4. Match each addition statement with its sum.

(−6) + (−5)   +11

(−6) + (+5)   −11

(+6) + (−5)   +1

(+6) + (+5)   −1

5. Add, using a method of your choice.
Use a different method to check your work.

a) $(-1) + (+5) = $ _____

b) $(-8) + (+2) = $ _____

c) $(-8) + (-6) = $ _____

d) $(+2) + (-5) + (-3) = $ _____

6. Kim earned $24 babysitting.
He spent $7 buying lunch at school.

How much does Kim have left? _____

7. Create a problem that can be solved using integer addition.
Show the solution.
Here are some possible ideas.
- temperature change
- elevation change
- bank balance

_____

_____

_____

_____

8. Play this game with 2 to 4 people.
You will need a deck of cards with face cards removed, paper, and pencil.

Red cards are negative. Black cards are positive.

Deal 2 cards to each player.
➤ Players find the sum of their 2 numbers.
➤ If a player has a sum of 0, he or she is "out."
➤ Remaining players each take 1 card from the deck.
   Add this number to the previous sum.
➤ Any player with a total of 0 is "out."
➤ Play continues until 1 player remains.
➤ The last player in the game wins.

Quick Review

➤ To model subtraction using tiles, begin by modelling the first number.
Then, take away tiles that model the number to be subtracted.
If there are not enough tiles to take away, add zero pairs.

Use tiles to subtract. (–2) – (–4)
Model –2. 　`−` `−`

There are not enough tiles to take away –4.

You need more `−` tiles.

Add 2 zero pairs.

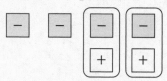

Now take away 4 `−` tiles.

There are 2 `+` tiles left.

These model +2, so we write:

(–2) – (–4) = +2

Practice

1. Use tiles to subtract. (+2) – (+5)
Start with 2 `+` tiles.　　　　　　`+` `+`

a) Can you take away +5 from +2? _____

b) Add zero pairs until you can take away 5 `+` tiles.

c) So, (+2) – (+5) = _____

2. Use tiles to subtract. (−3) − (+4)

    a) Model −3 with 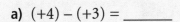 tiles.

    b) Can you take away +4 from −3? _____

    c) Add zero pairs until you can take away 4 $\boxed{+}$ tiles .

    d) So, (−3) − (+4) = _____

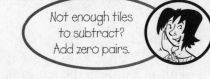

HINT

Not enough tiles to subtract? Add zero pairs.

3. Draw tiles to represent each difference.
Then complete the subtraction equation.

    a) (+4) − (+3) = _____   **b)** (−2) − (−5) = _____

$\boxed{+}$ $\boxed{+}$ $\boxed{+}$ $\boxed{+}$

    c) (+1) − (+6) = _____   **d)** (+5) − (+3) − (+1) = _____

4. Subtract.

    a) (−7) − (−5) = _____   **b)** (+3) − (+8) = _____

    c) (+6) − (−4) = _____   **d)** (+4) − (+3) − (−2) = _____

5. Subtract. Then complete the subtraction equation.

    C. (+3) − (+5) = _____   E. (−2) − (−1) = _____   L. (+3) − (−1) = _____

    I. (+3) − (+3) = _____   H. (−2) − (+1) = _____   T. (+3) − (−3) = _____

    O. (+3) − (+1) = _____   N. (−2) − (+3) = _____   R. (+3) − (−5) = _____

Why is it always warm in Brazil and Peru? Fill in the corresponding letters to find out.

They are ____ ____ ____   ____ ____ ____ ____ ____ !
     −5   +2   +6   −2   −3   0   +4   −1

Quick Review

➤ You can subtract integers using a number line.

When you subtract, you move in the opposite direction of addition.
Subtraction is the opposite of addition.

Subtract. (−1) − (−3)
Start at −1.
This is 1 unit to the left of 0.

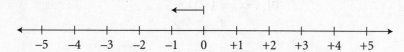

Then, move in the opposite direction of adding (−3).

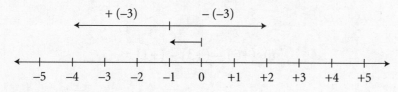

So, (−1) − (−3) = +2

➤ The result is the same as adding the opposite integer.
(−1) − (−3) is the same as (−1) + (+3). Both equal +2.

Practice

1. Use the number line to subtract. (+3) − (+5)

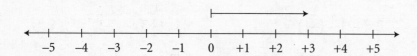

a) Start at 0. Move 3 units to the _____.

b) Then move _____ units left.

c) (+3) − (+5) = _____

2. Use a number line to subtract.

a) (+3) – (+4) = _____

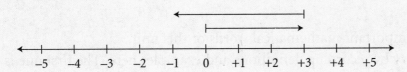

b) (–2) – (+3) = _____

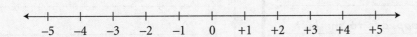

c) (–1) – (–6) = _____

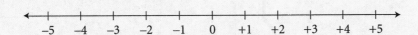

3. Rewrite each subtraction as addition of the opposite integer. Then solve.

a) (+2) – (–6) = (+2) + (+6)

       = _____

b) (–2) – (–4) = (–2) + _____

       = _____

c) (+1) – (+5) = _____ + _____

       = _____

d) (–12) – (+9) = _____ + _____

       = _____

4. Subtract.

a) (+4) – (+7) = _____

b) (+6) – (–5) = _____

c) 0 – (–4) = _____

d) (–10) – (–2) = _____

e) (+2) – (+12) = _____

f) (–1) – (–10) = _____

> **Tip**
> *Use a second method to check your answer.*

5. a) Asad's golf score changed from 2 above par to 3 below par.
How did his score change?

(–3) – (+2) = _____   It decreased by _____.

b) Murphy's golf score changed from 1 below par to 5 above par.
How did his score change?

It _____ by _____.

In Your Words

Here are some of the important mathematical words of this unit.
Build your own glossary by recording definitions and examples here. The first one is done for you.

negative number *any number*
less than zero
A negative number appears to the left
of zero on a number line.
For example, −2, −18, and −4000 are
negative numbers.

integer

positive integer

negative integer

opposite integers

zero pair

List other mathematical words you need to know.

Unit Review

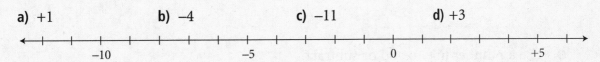

LESSON

9.1 **1.** Show each integer on the number line.

a) +1 b) −4 c) −11 d) +3

←———┼———┼———┼———┼———┼———┼———┼———┼———┼———┼———┼———┼———┼———┼———┼———→
              −10   −5   0   +5

9.2 **2. a)** Place either < or > between the integers.

i) +1 _____ −2 ii) −8 _____ 0 iii) −11 _____ −18

b) Order all the integers in part a from least to greatest.

_____, _____, _____, _____, _____, _____

9.3 **3.** Write the integer modelled by each set of tiles.

a)
| + | + | + | + |

| + | − | + | + | _____

b)
| + | − | + | − |

| − | − | − | _____

4. Draw tiles to model −2 three more ways.

HINT

Adding or removing zero pairs does not change the integer being modelled.

9.4 **5.** Use tiles to add.

a) (+6) + (−5) = _____

| + | + | + | + | + | + |

b) (−1) + (−3) + (+2) = _____

9.5 **6.** What type of integer do you get when you add two negative integers? Explain how you know.

_____

_____

_____

197

9.6 **7.** Use tiles to add or subtract.

a) (+3) – (–2) = _____

| + | | + | | + |

b) (+5) + (–4) – (–3) = _____

9.7 **8.** Use a number line to add or subtract.

a) (+5) + (–8) = _____

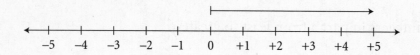

b) (–4) – (–7) = _____

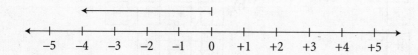

c) (–4) + (+6) + (–3) = _____

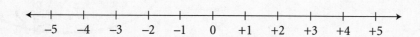

d) (–3) – (–7) + (–8) = _____

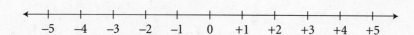

9. Calculate each difference.

a) The temperature went from –7°C to +8°C.

_____

b) The temperature went from +20°C to +3°C.

_____

Just for Fun

Pharaoh's Staircase

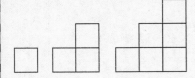

You need 6 blocks to make a *Pharaoh's Staircase* with a height of 3 blocks.

You will need _____ blocks for a staircase with a height of 5 blocks.

You will need _____ blocks for a staircase with a height of 10 blocks.

Pairing Up

Can you find the missing numbers in the pairs of numbers?

6	3	5	1
4		5	9

5	8	7	11
3	6		9

3	5	8	
6	10		20

Heading Home

A Game for **2**

Use the dot grid. Start at the centre, O.

You may move up, down, left, or right, but not diagonally.

Player A draws an arrow 1 grid unit long in any direction from O.

Player B adds an arrow 1 grid unit long to Player A's arrow to make a continuous route. Take turns drawing arrows.

Player A tries to head home to A, while player B tries to head home to B.

You may not go over a dot more than once.

The first player to get home wins.

A ● ● ● ● ● ●
● ● ● ● ● ●
● ● ● ● ● ●
● ● ● ●O ● ● ●
● ● ● ● ● ●
● ● ● ● ● ●
● ● ● ● ● ●B

199

Skills You'll Need

Order of Operations

Perform operations inside the brackets first.
Next, divide and multiply in order from left to right.
Then add and subtract in order from left to right.

> The letters B, D, M, A, and S can help you remember the order of operations.
> B—Brackets
> D, M—Divide, Multiply
> A, S—Add, Subtract

Example 1

Simplify.

a) $10 - 3 \times 2$

b) $12 \div (5 + 1)$

c) $6 \times 2 \div 3 + 1$

Solution

a) $10 - 3 \times 2 = 10 - 6$ Multiply first.
$= 4$ Then subtract.

b) $12 \div (5 + 1) = 12 \div 6$ Add inside the brackets first.
$= 2$ Then divide.

c) $6 \times 2 \div 3 + 1 = 12 \div 3 + 1$ Multiply first.
$= 4 + 1$ Then divide.
$= 5$ Then add.

✓ Check

1. Simplify.

a) $12 - 2 \times 4$

$= 12 - \underline{\hspace{3cm}}$

$= \underline{\hspace{3cm}}$

b) $20 \div (2 + 3)$

$= 20 \div \underline{\hspace{3cm}}$

$= \underline{\hspace{3cm}}$

c) $12 \div 6 \times 5 + 4$

$= \underline{\hspace{2cm}} \times 5 + 4$

$= \underline{\hspace{3cm}}$

d) $10 + 4 \div 2$

$= 10 + \underline{\hspace{3cm}}$

$= \underline{\hspace{3cm}}$

e) $(9 - 5) \times 6$

$= \underline{\hspace{2cm}} \times 6$

$= \underline{\hspace{3cm}}$

f) $5 + 2 \times 3 - 4$

$= 5 + \underline{\hspace{3cm}}$

$= \underline{\hspace{3cm}}$

Graphing on a Coordinate Grid

An ordered pair, such as (5, 3), tells you the position of a point on a grid.
The first number is the horizontal distance from the origin, O.
The second number is the vertical distance from the origin, O.
The numbers of an ordered pair are also called the **coordinates** of a point.

Example 2

Graph the points A(5, 3), B(2, 0), and C(0, 4) on a grid.

Solution

To plot point A, start at 5 on the horizontal axis, then move up 3.

To plot point B, start at 2 on the horizontal axis, then move up 0. Point B is on the horizontal axis.

To plot point C, start at 0 on the horizontal axis, then move up 4. Point C is on the vertical axis.

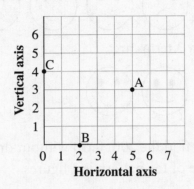

✓ Check

2. Write the ordered pair for each point on the grid.

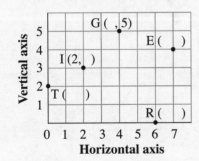

3. Plot and label these points:
   A(0, 5), B(2, 4), E(4, 3), R(5, 0)

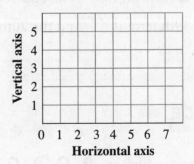

4. The graph shows the number of bracelets Jan can make over time.
   a) How many bracelets can Jan make in 3 h? _____

   b) How long will it take to make 10 bracelets? _____

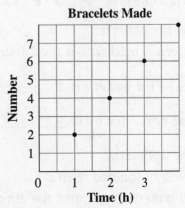

Bracelets Made

Quick Review

➤ You can make patterns using figures and numbers.
Each figure or number in a pattern is called a **term**.
Here is a pattern.

The next 3 terms are:

➤ You can find the 20th term without drawing all 20 terms.
The core of the pattern is 3 figures.

To find the 20th term, you must find which of the first 3 terms it matches.

Think of multiples of 3: 3, 6, 9, 12, 15, 18, …

The 3rd, 6th, 9th, 12th, 15th, and 18th terms are all ☺.

So the 19th term is ☺ and the 20th term is ☹.

Practice

1. This pattern continues. **P O P O P O P...**

a) Describe the pattern.
The pattern is made up of the 2 letters P and O, which repeat in that order.

The core of the pattern is: P _____

b) Write the next 3 terms. O _____ _____

c) Write the 20th term.
Every even-numbered term is O.
Since 20 is an even number, the 20th term is _____.

2. This pattern continues. **R O C K R O C K R**...

a) Describe the pattern.

The pattern is made up of the 4 letters _____ .

The core of the pattern is: _____

b) Write the next 3 terms of the pattern: _____ _____ _____

c) Write the 31st term.

Since there are _____ terms that repeat, compare with multiples of _____ .

Pattern: Every 4th term is K.

Multiples of 4 :   _____, _____, _____, _____, _____, _____, _____, ...

So, the 28th term is K, and the 29th term is _____ .

The 30th term is _____ .

The 31st term is _____ .

3. This pattern continues.

a) Describe the pattern.
The pattern is made up of 3 squares with 1, 2, and 3 dots, which repeat in that order.
The core of the pattern is:

b) Sketch the next 3 terms.

c) Sketch the 26th term.

203

4. This pattern continues. ⊔⊏⊓⊐⊔⊏⊓⊐⊔⊏ ...

a) Describe the pattern.

b) Sketch the next 3 terms.

c) Sketch the 30th term.

5. This pattern continues. 5, 7, 9, 11, ...

a) To find each term, add _____ to the preceding term.

b) The next 3 terms are: 11 + 2 = _____, _____ + 2 = _____, _____ + _____ = _____

c) Find the 12th term.

Since the terms increase by 2 each time, compare with multiples of 2.

Pattern: 5 , 7 , 9 , 11 , _____, _____, _____, ...

Multiples of 2:   _____, _____, _____, _____, _____, _____, _____, ...

Each term in the pattern is 3 more than a multiple of 2.

The 1st term: $1 \times 2 + 3 = 5$

The 2nd term: $2 \times 2 + 3 =$ _____

The 3rd term: $3 \times 2 +$ _____ $=$ _____

The 4th term: $4 \times$ _____ $+$ _____ $=$ _____, and so on

The 12th term: $12 \times$ _____ $+$ _____ $=$ _____

KEY TO SUCCESS

If you can solve a simple problem using a pattern, you can solve a similar problem that is more difficult by looking for a similar pattern.

6. This pattern continues. 7, 12, 17, 22, …

   a) To find each term, add _____ to the preceding term.

   b) The next 3 terms are: 22 + 5 = _____, _____ + 5 = _____, _____ + _____ = _____

   c) Find the 8th term.

     Since the terms increase by _____ each time, compare with multiples of _____ .

     Pattern: 7 , 12 , 17 , 22 , _____, _____, _____, …

     Multiples of _____: _____, _____, _____, _____, _____, _____, _____, …

     Each term in the pattern is _____ more than a multiple of _____ .

     The 1st term: $1 \times$ _____ $+ 2 = 7$

     The 2nd term: $2 \times$ _____ $+$ _____ $= 12$

     The 3rd term: $3 \times$ _____ $+$ _____ $=$ _____

     The 4th term: $4 \times$ _____ $+$ _____ $=$ _____, and so on

     The 8th term: _____ $\times$ _____ $+$ _____ $=$ _____

H I N T

Ask yourself, "What must I multiply by, and then what do I add?"

7. This pattern continues. 6, 10, 14, 18, …

   a) Describe the pattern. _____ .

   b) Write the next 4 terms. _____, _____, _____, _____

   c) Find the 10th term. _____

8. This pattern continues. 5, 8, 11, 14, …
Find the 10th and the 20th terms.

_____

9. You can make this pattern out of toothpicks.

How many toothpicks will you need to make 20 triangles?

_____

Quick Review

➤ You can use a table and a graph to illustrate number patterns.

Here is a number pattern: 6, 10, 14, 18, …

In this pattern, term 1 has a value of 6, term 2 has a value of 10, and so on.

Suppose that an Input/Output machine created the numbers in the pattern.

You can display the numbers from the machine in a table.

The Input number is the term number
and the Output number is the term value.

The Input number starts at 1
and increases by 1 each time.

Input	Output
1	6
2	10
3	14
4	18

The Output number starts at 6
and increases by 4 each time.

Compare the Output numbers with multiples of 4.

Output numbers: 6,   10,   14,   18, …

Multiples of 4:   4,   8,   12,   16, …

Each Output number is 2 more than 4 times an Input number.

The 1st Output number: $1 \times 4 + 2 = 6$

The 2nd Output number: $2 \times 4 + 2 = 10$

The 3rd Output number: $3 \times 4 + 2 = 14$

The 4th Output number: $4 \times 4 + 2 = 18$, and so on

The rule for this pattern is:
Multiply the Input number by 4, then add 2.

The graph of the data in the table also
shows the pattern.

The points lie on a straight line.

To move from one point to the next,
move 1 unit right and 4 units up.

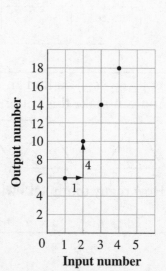

Practice

1. The Output column in each table shows a pattern. Complete each table.

a)

Input	Output
1	10
2	12
3	14
4	16
5	
6	
7	

b)

Input	Output
1	6
2	11
3	16
4	21
5	
6	
7	

c)

Input	Output
1	8
2	7
3	6
4	5
5	
6	
7	

2. The Output column of the table shows a pattern.

a) Complete the table.

Input	Output
1	3
2	5
3	7
4	9
5	
6	
7	

b) Graph the data in the table.

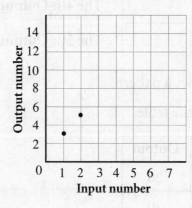

c) How can you find an Output number when you know an Input number?

Output numbers: 3 , 5 , 7 , 9 , _____, _____, _____, ...

Multiples of 2: _____, _____, _____, _____, _____, _____, _____, ...

Each Output number is _____ more than _____ times its Input number.

To find an Output number, multiply its Input number by _____, then add _____.

3. Complete the table. Multiply each Input number by 5.

Input	Output
1	5
2	
3	
4	
5	

The 1st Output number: $\qquad 1 \times 5 = 5$

The 2nd Output number: $\underline{\hspace{1cm}} \times 5 = 10$

The 3rd Output number: $\underline{\hspace{1cm}} \times 5 = \underline{\hspace{1cm}}$

The 4th Output number: $\underline{\hspace{1cm}} \times \underline{\hspace{1cm}} = \underline{\hspace{1cm}}$

The 5th Output number: $\underline{\hspace{1cm}} \times \underline{\hspace{1cm}} = \underline{\hspace{1cm}}$

4. Complete the table. Multiply each Input number by 3, then add 2.

Input	Output
1	5
2	
3	
4	
5	

The 1st Output number: $\qquad 1 \times 3 + 2 = 5$

The 2nd Output number: $\qquad 2 \times 3 + 2 = \underline{\hspace{1cm}}$

The 3rd Output number: $\underline{\hspace{1cm}} \times \underline{\hspace{1cm}} + 2 = \underline{\hspace{1cm}}$

The 4th Output number: $\underline{\hspace{1cm}} \times \underline{\hspace{1cm}} + \underline{\hspace{1cm}} = \underline{\hspace{1cm}}$

The 5th Output number: $\underline{\hspace{1cm}} \times \underline{\hspace{1cm}} + \underline{\hspace{1cm}} = \underline{\hspace{1cm}}$

5. The table shows a pattern.

a) Complete the table.

Input	Output
1	20
2	30
3	40
4	
5	
6	

b) Graph the data in the table.

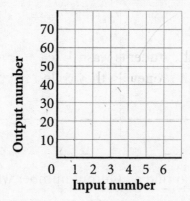

20 +5

c) How can you find an Output number when you know an Input number?

_____

6. The student council decides to wash cars to raise money for charity. The council charges $2.50 per car.

a) Complete the table.

Number of Cars	Money Collected
10	
20	
30	
40	
50	

b) Graph the data in the table.

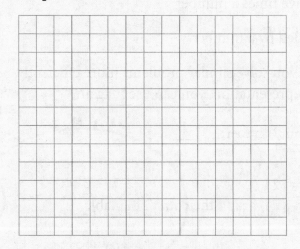

Tip

Identify the Input number and the Output number. Give the graph a title.

c) Suppose the students wash 12 cars. How much money do they collect? Explain.

_____

_____

_____

d) How much money will be raised if the students wash 80 cars? Extend the table in part a 3 more rows.

_____

_____

Number of Cars	Money Collected

Quick Review

➤ **Algebraic expressions** contain **variables** such as **x** and **n**.
x and **n** can represent any numbers you choose.

Here are some examples of algebraic expressions and what they mean.

$x + 5$:   A number increased by 5

$n - 3$:   A number decreased by 3

$5x$:   Five times a number

$5n + 3$:   Three more than five times a number

$\dfrac{100}{n}$:   One hundred divided by a number

➤ Algebraic expressions can help you solve similar problems more efficiently.
Once you know the algebraic representation, you can use it again,
even if the numbers change.

Suppose you earn $8 per hour.

For 3 hours, you earn: $3 \times \$8 = \$24$

For t hours, you earn: $t \times \$8 = 8t$ dollars

H I N T

If you see how to solve a problem using numbers, then you can write an algebraic expression for the problem. Replace the number that changes with a variable.

Practice

1. Match each algebraic expression with its meaning.

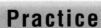

$6 + x$ Five less than a number

$4n$ One more than double a number

$1 + 2t$ Five decreased by a number

$5 - p$ Four times a number

$s - 5$ Three times a number decreased by four

$3g - 4$ Six more than a number

2. Write an algebraic expression for each statement.
Use the variable *n*.

    a) Ten times a number _____   **b)** Double a number _____

    c) A number divided by four _____   **d)** Six less than a number _____

    e) Three more than ten times a number _____

    f) Six less than ten times a number _____

3. True or False? If a sentence is false, then write the correct algebraic expression.

    a) Five decreased by a number can be written as $5 - n$. T ✓

    b) Twenty-five divided by a number can be written as $\dfrac{25}{n}$. T ✓

    c) A number divided by five, then add 3 can be written as $\dfrac{n}{3} + 5$. F $\dfrac{n}{5} + 3$ ✓

    d) Subtract two from double a number can be written as $2(n - 2)$. F $(2-2n$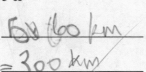

$2n - 2$

4. A clerk earns \$12 an hour.
Find how much the clerk earns for each period of time.

    a) 5 h   **b)** 8 h   **c)** *p* hours

$5 \times$ <u>12\$</u> $8 \times 12\$$ 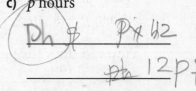

60 \$ ✓   96\$ ✓   Ph $12p\$$

5. A car travels at an average speed of 60 km/h.
Find how far it will travel after each length of time.

    a) 3 h   **b)** 5 h   **c)** *x* hours

   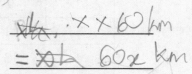

$3 \times$ 60 km   5 × 60 km   x × 60 km

= 180 km   = 300 km   = 60x km

6. Find the area and perimeter of a rectangle that is 10 cm long and 5 cm wide.

$A = bh$

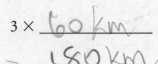

5×10× 5×10 = 2500

= 2500

$P = 2(b + h)$

5+10+5+10 = 35.

= 35

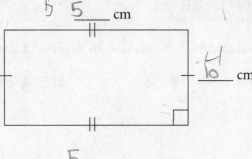

B   5 cm

10

10 cm

5

Quick Review

➤ When you replace a variable with a number in an algebraic expression, you **evaluate** the expression.

Evaluate the algebraic expression $2n + 5$ when $n = 3$.

Replace n with 3.

$$2n + 5 = 2(3) + 5$$
$$= 6 + 5$$
$$= 11$$

HINT

Remember that $2n$ means 2 times a number n. Remember the order of operations: Multiply first ($2 \times n$), then add ($+ 5$).

➤ You can create a pattern of numbers using the expression $2n + 5$ by substituting consecutive numbers, such as, 1, 2, 3, 4, and so on, for n:

When $n = 1$, $2n + 5 = 2 \times 1 + 5 = 7$
When $n = 2$, $2n + 5 = 2 \times 2 + 5 = 9$
When $n = 3$, $2n + 5 = 2 \times 3 + 5 = 11$
When $n = 4$, $2n + 5 = 2 \times 4 + 5 = 13$

You can show the pattern of numbers in an Input/Output table.

Input n	Output $2n + 5$
1	7
2	9
3	11
4	13

The values of n are the Input numbers and the values of $2n + 5$ are the Output numbers.

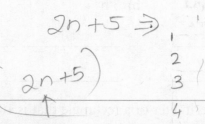

Practice

1. Evaluate each expression by replacing z with 10.

a) $z + 5 = 10 + 5$
$= 15$

b) $8 + z = 8 + 10$
$= 18$

c) $z - 6 = 10 - 6$
$= 4$

d) $15 - z = 15 - 10$
$= 5$

e) $3z = 3(10)$
$= 30$

f) $5z = 5(10)$
$= 50$

212

2. Evaluate each expression by replacing *n* with 2.

a) $2n + 3$

$= 2 \times \underline{2} + 3$

$= \underline{4} + 3$

$= \underline{7}$

b) $20 - 5n$

$= \underline{20} - 5 \times 2$

$= \underline{5 \times 2 - 10}$

$= \underline{20 - 10 = 10}$

Tip

Use the order of operations:
B—Brackets
D, M—Divide, Multiply
A, S—Add, Subtract

c) $\dfrac{(n + 8)}{5}$

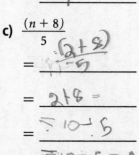

$= \underline{2 + 8 =}$

$= \underline{10 \div 5}$

$= 10 - 5 = 2$

d) $\dfrac{(14 - n)}{2}$

$= \underline{(14 - 2}$

$= \underline{12}$

$= \underline{12 \div 2}$

$= 6$

3. a) Evaluate the expression $3n + 1$.

When $n = 1$, $3n + 1 = 3 \times 1 + 1 = \underline{4}$

When $n = 2$, $3n + 1 = 3 \times 2 + 1 = \underline{7}$

When $n = 3$, $3n + 1 = 3 \times 3 + \underline{3} = \underline{12}$

When $n = 4$, $3n + 1 = 3 \times \underline{4} + \underline{1} = \underline{13}$

When $n = 5$, $3n + 1 = 3 \times \underline{5} + \underline{1} = \underline{16}$

b) Complete the table. Use your results from part a.

Input *n*	Output $3n + 1$
1	4
2	7
3	12
4	13
5	16

KEY TO SUCCESS

Evaluating algebraic expressions is an important skill. Carpenters, computer scientists, designers, electricians, and auto mechanics all use this skill to solve problems on the job.

4. Complete each table.

a)

Input x	Output $x + 5$
1	6
2	7
3	8
4	9
5	10

b)

Input x	Output $10 - x$
1	9
2	8
3	7
4	6
5	5

5. Complete each table.

a)

Input	Output
1	0
2	1
3	2
4	3
5	4
x	5

$1 - 1 = 0$
$2 - 1 = 1$
$3 - 1 = 2$
$4 - 1 = 3$
$5 - 1 = 4$
$x - 1 =$
$(x - 1)$

$5 - 1$

b)

Input	Output
1	4
2	8
3	12
4	16
5	20
x	24

$3 = 12$
3×4
$6 - 1$
$x \times 4$ $4x$
$10 -$
n

6. Emily works for $6 per hour.

a) How much will she earn if she works 8 hours? __48$__

b) How much will she earn if she works 10 hours? __60$__

c) Write an algebraic expression for her earnings for t hours. __6(t)__

d) Evaluate the expression in part c by replacing t with 12. __6(12) = 72__

e) What is the meaning of your answer in part d? __6 × 12 = 72__

__it said reaplace t with 12__

f) Emily earned $90 working on the weekend.
How many hours did she work?

90 th

$90 = 6 \times h$

$90 = 6x$

$x = 90/6$

7. Albert is organizing an end of term party.
The cost of renting a hall for an evening is $100.
The cost of food is $8 per person.

a) How much will the party cost if 20 people attend? 50 people attend?

$$20 = 8 \times 20 = 160\$$$
$$50 = 8 \times 50 = 400\$$$

b) Write an algebraic expression for the cost of the party if *n* people attend.

$$100\$ + 8n$$

c) Suppose Albert decides to hire a DJ for the party.
The DJ charges $250 for the evening.
What is the new cost of the party when *n* people attend?

$$100\$ + 250\$ + 8n = 350\$ + 8n$$

d) Suppose the cost of food increases by $2 per person.
Write an expression for the total cost of the party with a DJ for *n* people.

$$100 + 250 + 10n = 350 + 10n\$$$

e) The new food price is in effect.
How much will the party with a DJ cost for 40 people?
Show your work.

$$350 + 10n \, ^{40}$$
$$= 350 + 10 \times 40$$
$$= 10 \times 40$$
$$= 400$$
$$= 400 + 350\$$$
$$= 750\$$$

8. A value for *x* is substituted in each expression to get the number in the box.
Find each value of *x*.

a) $x + 5$ | 8 |
$$= 8 + 5$$
$$= 13$$
$$= 2x + 3 =$$

b) $12 - x$ | 5 | $12 - 5 = 7$

c) $2x + 3$ | 7 | $= 17$

d) $7x - 2$ | 54 | $7 \times 54 - 2 = 518$

e) $26 - 3x$ | 11 | $26 - 3 \times 11$
$$= 3 \times 11$$
$$= 33$$
$$= 33 - 26$$
$$= 07$$

f) $\frac{x}{5} + 4$ | 13 | $\frac{13}{5} + 4$
$$\frac{2R3}{}$$
$$= 2 + 3$$
$$= 5 + 4$$
$$= 9$$

Quick Review

➤ An equation is a statement that two expressions are equal.

$2x + 1$ is an algebraic expression.
7 is an expression.
$2x + 1 = 7$ is an equation.

This equation can be expressed in words as:
One more than double a number is seven.

➤ Here's how to write equations from sentences.

1. Choose a letter for the variable.
2. Write an algebraic expression to represent the relationship described.
3. Put an equal sign between the expressions.

Five more than a number comes to 20.
Let p represent the number.
Five more than p: $p + 5$
The equation is: $p + 5 = 20$

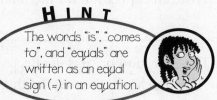

HINT
The words "is", "comes to", and "equals" are written as an equal sign (=) in an equation.

A number subtracted from ten equals 4.
Let x represent the number.
x subtracted from ten: $10 - x$
The equation is: $10 - x = 4$

A number divided by two is 8.
Let n represent the number.

n divided by two: $\frac{n}{2}$

The equation is: $\frac{n}{2} = 8$

Practice

1. Match each sentence with an equation.

A number divided by three is 4. $20 - n = 6$

Twenty subtract a number equals 6. $2n + 3 = 11$

Nine subtract one-half a number comes to 6. $\frac{n}{3} = 4$

Three added to double a number is 11. $9 - \frac{n}{2} = 6$

2. Write an equation for each sentence.
Let n represent the number.

   a) Eight less than a number is 2. $n -$ _____ $=$ _____

   b) One-half a number equals 5. _____

   c) Four more than double a number is 20. _____

   d) Six plus three times a number is 9. _____

3. Write each equation as a sentence.

   a) $n - 6 = 12$

   _____

   b) $\frac{x}{2} = 10$

   _____

   c) $2p + 10 = 14$

   _____

4. Write an equation for each sentence.
Let x represent the number.

   a) Three more than a number comes to 12. _____

   b) Three less than a number is 12. _____

   c) Three times a number equals 12. _____

   d) Three more than three times a number is 12. _____

   e) Three subtracted from three times a number equals 12. _____

5. Write an equation for each problem.

   a) The cost of 2 adult's tickets at $5 each and n child's tickets at $3 each is $25.

   _____

   b) William's age 4 years ago was 12.

   _____

   c) The perimeter of a square with side length s is 28.

   _____

Quick Review

➤ When you **solve an equation** you find the value of the variable that makes the equation true.

You can solve an equation by *systematic trial* or by *inspection*.

➤ **Solve by Systematic Trial**

$2x + 3 = 17$

Tip

Each trial provides information to guide you in choosing a value for the next trial.

Choose a value for x and substitute.

Try $x = 10$; then $2 \times 10 + 3 = 23$ 23 is too large. Try a lesser value.
Try $x = 5$; then $2 \times 5 + 3 = 13$ 13 is too small. Try a value between 5 and 10.
Try $x = 6$; then $2 \times 6 + 3 = 15$ 15 is too small. Try a value between 6 and 10.
Try $x = 7$; then $2 \times 7 + 3 = 17$ $x = 7$ makes the equation true.

So, $x = 7$.

➤ **Solve by Inspection**

$20 - n = 5$

To solve the equation by inspection, ask yourself:
"What number subtracted from 20 gives 5?"

Since $20 - 15 = 5$, $n = 15$.

Some equations can be more difficult to solve by inspection.
Solve the equation $2x + 3 = 13$ by inspection.

You know that $10 + 3 = 13$

So $2x = 10$

Then ask yourself, "Two times what number gives 10?"
You know that $2 \times 5 = 10$.

You can check to see if 5 makes the equation true by substituting 5 for x:
$2 \times 5 + 3 = 13$

So, $x = 5$.

1. Solve by inspection.

   a) $2n = 12$ b) $x + 10 = 30$ c) $25 - p = 20$

   _____   _____   _____

   d) $x - 8 = 2$ e) $5n = 15$ f) $\frac{x}{2} = 5$

   _____   _____   _____

2. Solve the equation $2x + 5 = 37$ by systematic trial.

Input	Evaluate $2x + 5$	Too large or too small?
$x = 30$	$2 \times 30 + 5 = 65$	This is too large.
$x = 20$	$2 \times 20 + 5 = 45$	This is too large.
$x = 5$	$2 \times 5 + 5 = 15$	This is too small.
$x = 10$	$2 \times 10 + 5 =$	
$x = 15$	$2 \times 15 + 5 =$	

3. Solve.

   a) $3x = 60$ b) $x + 12 = 30$ c) $\frac{x}{5} = 9$ d) $5x - 4 = 26$

   _____   _____   _____   _____

4. Which value of n makes the equation $\frac{20}{n} + 5 = 9$ true? Circle your answer.

   a) $n = 1$ b) $n = 2$ c) $n = 4$ d) $n = 5$ e) $n = 10$ f) $n = 20$

5. Jasmine has 135 butterfly stickers.
   She gave 15 to her little sister and the rest to her friends.
   Each friend has 20 stickers. How many friends did she give stickers to?
   Fill in the missing expressions to create an equation you can solve.
   Let f represent the number of friends.

   _____ + _____ = _____
   number of   number of   total number of
   stickers to sister   stickers to friends   stickers

   Jasmine gave stickers to _____ friends.

In Your Words

Here are some of the important mathematical words of this unit.
Build your own glossary by recording definitions and examples here. The first one is done for you.

ordered pair *two numbers*

that tell the position of a point on a grid

For example, to plot the ordered pair

(2, 5), start at 2 on

the horizontal axis,

then move up 5 units.

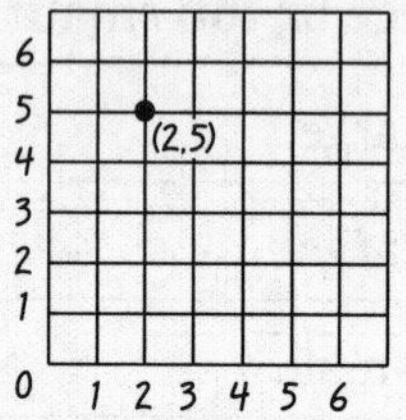

algebraic expression _____

_____

_____

_____

_____

_____

variable _____

_____

_____

_____

_____

evaluate _____

_____

_____

_____

_____

equation _____

_____

_____

_____

solve an equation _____

_____

_____

_____

_____

List other mathematical words you need to know.

_____

Unit Review

LESSON
10.1

1. This pattern continues.   . . .

   a) Draw the next 3 terms in the pattern.   **b)** Draw the 24th term.

2. This pattern continues. 7, 10, 13, 16, …

   a) Describe the pattern.

   _____

   b) Write the next 3 terms in the pattern. _____ , _____ , _____

   c) Write the 20th term.
   Pattern: 7,   10,   13,   16, …

   Compare with multiples of ____ : _____

   Each term is _____ more than a multiple of _____ .

   The 1st term: 1 × _____ + _____ = 7

   The 2nd term: 2 × _____ + _____ = 10

   The 3rd term: 3 × _____ + _____ = 13

   The 4th term: 4 × _____ + _____ = 16, and so on

   The 20th term: _____ × _____ + _____ = _____

10.2 **3.** This pattern continues. 4, 6, 8, 10, …

   a) Complete the table.   **b)** Graph the data in the table.

Input	Output
1	
2	
3	
4	
5	

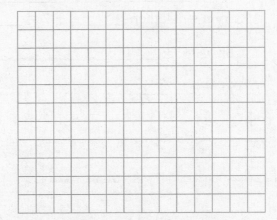

   c) How can you find an Output number when you know an Input number?

10.3 **4.** Write an algebraic expression for each statement.

    a) Three times a number _____

    b) Five less than a number _____

    c) Twenty divided by a number _____

    d) Seven more than four times a number _____

10.4 **5.** Evaluate each expression for $n = 5$.

    a) $n + 7 =$ _____   **b)** $10 - n =$ _____

    c) $2n + 3 =$ _____   **d)** $\dfrac{(n + 3)}{2} =$ _____

10.5 **6.** Write an equation for each statement.

    a) Four less than a number comes to sixteen. _____

    b) A number divided by five is ten. _____

    c) Five more than three times a number is eleven. _____

10.6 **7.** Solve by inspection.

    a) $x + 5 = 20$ _____   **b)** $5x = 40$ _____

8. Solve by systematic trial.

    a) $n + 7 = 40$

        Try $n = 30$; then $30 + 7 = 37$ This is too small.

        Try $n = 35$; then _____ $+ 7 =$ _____   This is too _____

        Try $n = 34$; then _____ $+ 7 =$ _____   _____

        Try $n = 33$; _____   _____

        So, $n =$ _____.

    b) $2n + 3 = 25$

Just for Fun

Integer Darts

One way to score a 0 with 4 darts using this dart board is: –2, –2, –1, 5

Find 4 different ways to score 0 with

3 darts: _____

4 darts: _____

_____

5 darts: _____

_____

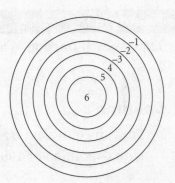

Number Shuffle

Make a set of 9 cards.
On each card, print one of the digits from 1 to 9.

Shuffle the cards and deal out 5.
Use the first 4 cards, together with some of the operation symbols or brackets
+, –, ×, ÷, or ( )
to create an expression equal to the value of the last card. For example:

| 2 | 5 | 8 | 1 | 4 |

$8 - 5 + 2 - 1 = 4$; $8 \div (5 - 1) + 2 = 4$

Play on your own, or race your friends.

In Between

A Game for 2

Remove the face cards from a deck of playing cards. Black cards are positive and red cards are negative.

Deal 5 cards to each player.
Player A selects 2 cards from her hand and places them face up.
Player B must find a card in his hand that is *in between* Player A's 2 cards.
Player B gets 1 point if he has a card in between, then takes the next turn.
If not, Player A gets a point, and takes the next turn.

Continue until all the cards are used.
The player with the most points wins.

Skills You'll Need

Converting Fractions and Decimals to Percents

To convert a fraction to a decimal, you can either
- try to write an equivalent fraction with denominator 100, then express the fraction as a decimal, or
- divide the numerator by the denominator.

To convert a decimal to a percent, multiply by 100.

Tip

To multiply a decimal number by 100, move the decimal point two places to the right.

Example

Express each fraction as a decimal, then as a percent.

a) $\frac{3}{25}$

b) $\frac{21}{40}$

Solution

a) Find an equivalent fraction with denominator 100.

$$\frac{3}{25} \overset{\times 4}{\underset{\times 4}{=}} \frac{12}{100}$$

$$\frac{12}{100} = 0.12$$

$$= 12\%$$

b) Divide the numerator by the denominator.

$$\frac{21}{40} = 21 \div 40$$

$$= 0.525$$

$$= 52.5\%$$

✓ Check

1. Express each fraction as a decimal, then as a percent.

a) $\frac{3}{4} = \frac{75}{100}$

$= \underline{\hspace{1.5cm}}$

$= \underline{\hspace{1.5cm}} \%$

b) $\frac{12}{25} = \frac{}{100}$

$= \underline{\hspace{1.5cm}}$

$= \underline{\hspace{1.5cm}} \%$

c) $\frac{9}{40} = \underline{\hspace{1.5cm}}$

$= \underline{\hspace{1.5cm}}$

d) $\frac{15}{16} = \underline{\hspace{1.5cm}}$

$= \underline{\hspace{1.5cm}}$

Quick Review

An **outcome** is a possible result of an experiment or action.

The outcomes of rolling a number cube labelled from 1 to 6 are:
1, 2, 3, 4, 5, 6

The outcomes of spinning the pointer on this spinner are:
white, black, striped, dotted

You can use a tree diagram to show the outcomes of experiments with 2 or more actions.

What are the possible outcomes when spinning this spinner, and tossing a coin?

List the outcomes of spinning the spinner. For each spinner outcome, list the outcomes of tossing the coin.

There are 8 possible outcomes.

Spinner	Coin	Outcomes
White	Heads	White, Heads
White	Tails	White, Tails
Black	Heads	Black, Heads
Black	Tails	Black, Tails
Striped	Heads	Striped, Heads
Striped	Tails	Striped, Tails
Dotted	Heads	Dotted, Heads
Dotted	Tails	Dotted, Tails

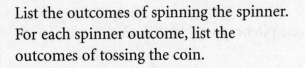

Practice

1. List the possible outcomes in each case.

   a) picking a number out of this hat

   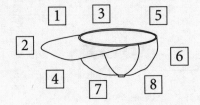

   b) choosing a piece of fruit

   _____

   _____

2. Each jar has one black (B) and one white (W) marble.

Jar 1   Jar 2

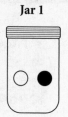 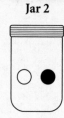

Complete the tree diagram to show the outcomes for picking a marble from each jar.
Then list the outcomes.

Jar 1   Jar 2   Outcomes

B
B   B   BB
_____   _____

W   B   _____
_____   _____

3. Coach Hanna has to choose one catcher and one pitcher from these choices.
Catcher: Carlos (C), Tim (T)
Pitcher: Elizabeth (E), André (A), Lise (L)

a) Complete the tree diagram for all possible combinations.

Catcher   Pitcher   Outcomes

E   CE
C   A   CA
_____   _____

E   _____
T   _____   _____
_____   _____

b) How many combinations have only males? _____

4. Ming wants to buy a ball and a plastic disc for his dog.
Both the ball and the plastic disc come in red (R), yellow (Y), or green (G).

a) Draw a tree diagram to show the possible combinations and outcomes.

H I N T

Use these headings to help you draw your tree diagram: Ball Colour, Disc Colour, Outcomes.

b) How many possible outcomes are there? _____

c) How many outcomes have both toys the same colour? _____

d) How many outcomes have at least one yellow toy? _____

e) How many outcomes do not have a red toy? _____

5. A test has 3 true (T) or false (F) questions.

a) Complete the tree diagram to show the possible outcomes for answering all 3 questions.

Question 1	Question 2	Question 3	Outcomes

```
                          T        TTT
              T <
                          F        TTF
      T <
              F <         ____      ____

                          ____      ____


              T <         ____      ____

                          ____      ____
      F <
                          ____      ____
          <
      ____      ____      ____      ____
```

b) How many outcomes have 3 true answers? _____

c) How many outcomes have exactly 2 true answers? _____

d) How many outcomes do not have all 3 answers the same? _____

227

6. Justina has these 2 spinners.
She spins the pointers of both spinners at the same time.
Each spinner has sectors of equal areas.

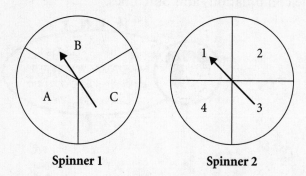

Spinner 1   Spinner 2

a) Draw a tree diagram to show all the possible outcomes.

b) How many possible outcomes are there? _____

c) How many outcomes have a vowel and an even number? _____

d) How many outcomes have a consonant and an odd number? _____

Quick Review

➤ The formula for the relative frequency of an outcome is:

$$\text{Relative frequency} = \frac{\text{Number of times an outcome occurs}}{\text{Number of times the experiment is conducted}}$$

Relative frequency is also called **experimental probability**.

Misha tosses a coin 50 times.
It lands heads 22 times and tails 28 times.

Relative frequency of heads is: Relative frequency of tails is:

$\frac{22}{50} = 0.44$ $\frac{28}{50} = 0.56$

$\quad = 44\%$ $\quad = 56\%$

➤ The sum of the relative frequencies of an experiment is 1.
For the coin toss experiment,

$$\text{relative frequency of heads} + \text{relative frequency of tails} = \frac{22}{50} + \frac{28}{50}$$

$$= 0.44 + 0.56$$

$$= 1$$

Practice

1. Adra tosses a coin 70 times. It lands heads 30 times.

   a) How many times does the coin land tails? _____

   b) Put a check mark beside each true statement.

      ____ Relative frequency of heads = 30×70

      ____ Relative frequency of heads = $\frac{30}{70}$

      ____ Relative frequency of tails = $\frac{70}{40}$

      ____ Relative frequency of tails = $\frac{40}{70}$

      ____ Relative frequency of tails = $\frac{40}{30}$

2. A number cube labelled 1 to 6 is rolled 100 times.

The number 1 shows 20 times.

The number 6 shows 25 times.

Find the relative frequency for each number.

Express your answers as fractions, decimals, and percents.

a) Rolling a 1

Relative frequency

$= \dfrac{\text{Number of times 1 occured}}{\text{Number of times experiment is conducted}}$

$=$ _____

$=$ _____

$=$ _____%

b) Rolling a 6

Relative frequency

$= \dfrac{\text{Number of times 6 occured}}{\text{Number of times experiment is conducted}}$

$=$ _____

$=$ _____

$=$ _____%

3. In a poll, 150 students are asked if they prefer rap or pop music.

95 students prefer rap.

55 students prefer pop.

Find the relative frequency for each type of music.

Express your answers as decimals and percents.

HINT

Round decimals to 3 decimal places and percents to 1 decimal place.

a) Rap

Relative frequency = _____

$\doteq$ _____

$\doteq$ _____%

b) Pop

Relative frequency = _____

$\doteq$ _____

$\doteq$ _____%

4. a) Complete the table by calculating the batting average for each baseball player.

Round each batting average to 2 decimal places.

Player	At Bats	Hits	Batting Average
Malcolm	62	32	
Ellie	55	29	
Tom	50	26	

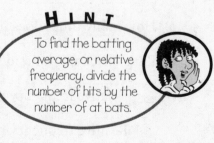

HINT

To find the batting average, or relative frequency, divide the number of hits by the number of at bats.

b) Who has the best batting average? _____

230

5. A spinner has three equal sectors coloured red, blue, and green.
Juan spins the pointer 40 times.
It lands on red 12 times and blue 13 times.
Find the relative frequencies for the pointer landing on each colour.
Round each answer to 3 decimal places if necessary.

a) Red

_____ = _____

b) Blue

_____

c) Green

_____

6. Jacqui tosses a paper cup 25 times.
The table shows the results.
Find the relative frequency for each case.

Position Cup Lands		Frequency
Right side up		$\|\|$
Upside down		$\cancel{\|\|\|\|}\ \|\|\|$
On its side		$\cancel{\|\|\|\|}\ \cancel{\|\|\|\|}\ \cancel{\|\|\|\|}$

a) The cup lands right side up.

$\dfrac{2}{25}$ = _____

b) The cup lands upside down.

_____

c) The cup lands on its side.

_____

d) The cup does not land right side up.

_____

7. Plot the relative frequencies in question 6 on this number line.

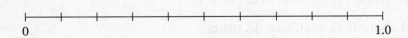

0   1.0

KEY TO SUCCESS

If you have difficulty solving a
problem in your homework, look in
your text for a similar example.
Look for a clue, one step at a time.

Quick Review

➤ The formula for the theoretical probability of an outcome is:

$$\text{Probability} = \frac{\text{Number of favourable outcomes}}{\text{Number of possible outcomes}}$$

> *A favourable outcome is any outcome that matches the desired result.*

The possible outcomes must be equally likely.

A bag contains 3 blue (B) balls, 5 red (R) balls, and 4 green (G) balls. You take a ball from the bag without looking and record the colour of the ball. Then you put the ball back into the bag.

Number of possible outcomes is: $3 + 5 + 4 = 12$

The probability of picking a blue ball is: $\frac{3}{12} = 0.25$

The probability of picking a red ball is: $\frac{5}{12} \doteq 0.42$

The probability of picking a green ball is: $\frac{4}{12} \doteq 0.33$

The probability of picking a blue or red ball is: $\frac{3}{12} + \frac{5}{12} = \frac{8}{12}$

$$\doteq 0.67$$

The probability of picking a blue or red ball is the same as picking a ball that is *not* green because there are 8 balls that are not green.

➤ You can use theoretical probability to predict the possible number of outcomes that will occur when an experiment is repeated.

Suppose the experiment above is done 100 times. Multiply each probability by 100 to predict the number of times each colour will be picked.

A blue ball will be picked about 0.25×100, or 25 times

A red ball will be picked about 0.42×100, or 42 times

A green ball will be picked about 0.33×100, or 33 times

➤ The sum of the probabilities of all outcomes of an experiment is 1.

Practice

1. A bag contains these fruit bars: 12 orange, 10 apple, and 13 banana.
A bar is picked at random from the bag.

    a) How many fruit bars are in the bag? _____

    b) Probability of picking an orange fruit bar $= \dfrac{\text{Number of orange bars}}{\text{Total number of bars}}$

$$= \text{_____}$$

    c) Probability of picking an apple fruit bar $=$

$$= \text{_____}$$

    d) Probability of picking a banana fruit bar $=$

$$= \text{_____}$$

    e) What is the probability that a bar picked is not an orange fruit bar?

        Probability =

$$=$$

$$=$$

2. Find each probability. Express your answers as decimals.
A charity sells 1000 tickets in a draw to win a new bicycle.

    a) Lee buys 5 tickets.
        Probability that Lee will win

        $=$

        $=$ _____

        $=$ _____

    b) Jasmine buys 20 tickets.
        Probability that Jasmine will win

        $=$

        $=$ _____

        $=$ _____

3. This table shows the hair colour of 30 people.
A person is picked at random.
Find each probability.

Hair Colour	Frequency
Brown	12
Blond	11
Red	5
Black	2

a) The person has black hair.

_____

b) The person has brown hair.

_____

c) The person does not have red hair.

_____

d) The person has blond or brown hair.

_____

4. A hat contains eight pieces of paper numbered 1 to 8.
Jamal picks a piece of paper from the hat and records the number.
Find each probability.
Express your answers as fractions.

a) The number is 7.

_____

b) The number is even.

_____

c) The number is a multiple of 3.

_____

d) The number is not a multiple of 3.

_____

5. Each letter in the word BRAVO is written on a separate card.
Sarah shuffles the cards and picks one without looking.
She puts the card back. She does this 50 times.

| B | R | A | V | O |

a) Find the probability of each outcome.

- choosing "O": _____

- choosing a vowel: _____

- choosing a consonant: _____

b) Predict how many times each outcome in part a will occur.

> **Tip**
> First, find the probability of each outcome. Then multiply the probability by the number of repeated actions.

Quick Review

➤ When probability is expressed as a percent, we use the word "chance".
Suppose the weather forecast is a 60% chance of rain.

Then, the probability of rain is: $\frac{60}{100} = 0.6$

➤ When an outcome is impossible, the probability of the outcome occurring is 0.
When an outcome is certain, the probability of the outcome occurring is 1.

➤ You can use tree diagrams to find probabilities.
The tree diagram shows the possible genders (F for female, M for male)
in a litter of 3 puppies.

Puppy 1	Puppy 2	Puppy 3	Outcomes

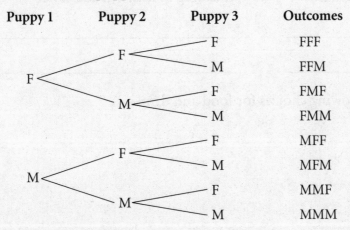

There are 8 possible outcomes.

There are 3 outcomes with exactly 2 females.
The probability of having exactly 2 females is:

$$\frac{\text{Number of outcomes with exactly 2 females}}{\text{Number of possible outcomes}} = \frac{3}{8}, \text{ or } 0.375$$

The chance of having exactly 2 females is 37.5%.

There are 4 outcomes with at least 2 males.
The probability of having at least 2 males is:

$$\frac{\text{Number of outcomes with at least 2 males}}{\text{Number of possible outcomes}} = \frac{4}{8}, \text{ or } 0.5$$

The chance of having at least 2 males is 50%.

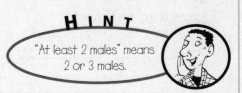

H I N T

"At least 2 males" means 2 or 3 males.

235

1. a) A quiz has 3 true (T) or false (F) questions.
The possible outcomes of a student answering 3 questions are:

b) How many outcomes are there? _____

c) Suppose a student guesses all 3 answers.
What is the chance of each outcome?

- Guessing 3 false answers

  Probability = _____, or _____

  The chance is _____%.

- Guessing at least 2 false answers

  _____

  _____

- Guessing exactly 2 true answers

  Probability = _____

  The chance is _____%.

- Guessing at least 1 true answer

  _____

  _____

2. A breakfast menu shows the following choices for food and drinks.

> **Breakfast Menu Items**
> Food: pancakes (P), omelette (O),
>   waffles (W)
> Drinks: coffee (C), milk (M),
>   juice (J)
> A breakfast is one choice of food and one choice of drink

a) Draw a tree diagram to show the
possible outcomes for a one food
and one drink breakfast.

b) A person chooses a breakfast at random.
What is the chance of choosing an
omelette and juice?

_____

_____

_____

3. Suppose you spin the pointers on these 2 spinners at the same time.

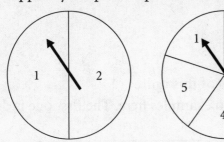

a) Draw a tree diagram to show the possible outcomes.

b) What is the chance of each outcome?

- Both pointers land on 1.

  _____

- Both pointers land on odd numbers.

  _____

- Both pointers land on the same number.

  _____

- The pointers land on two numbers that have a sum of 5.

  _____

4. A tennis coach needs to choose one player A and one player B for a tournament.
Player A choices: Chico, Angelina
Player B choices: Tina, Karl, Laura

Suppose the coach chooses the 2 players at random.
What is the chance of each outcome?

a) Both players are male: _____

b) Both players are female: _____

In Your Words

Here are some of the important mathematical words of this unit.
Build your own glossary by recording definitions and examples here. The first one is done for you.

theoretical probability _the_ likelihood of an outcome occurring when all outcomes are equally likely

$$\text{Theoretical Probability} = \frac{\text{Number of favourable outcomes}}{\text{Number of possible outcomes}}$$

For example, the probability of picking a red marble out of a bag containing 6 red marbles and 4 black marbles is: $\frac{6}{10}$

outcome _____

tree diagram _____

relative frequency _____

experimental probability _____

impossible outcome _____

List other mathematical words you need to know.

Unit Review

LESSON

11.1 **1.** The pointer of a spinner with 3 sectors labelled D, O, and G is spun twice. Complete the tree diagram to show the possible outcomes.

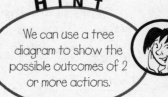

HINT

We can use a tree diagram to show the possible outcomes of 2 or more actions.

First Spin   Second Spin   Outcomes

                  D   DD

D   O   DO

11.2 **2.** A CD inspector finds that 2 out of 100 CDs are defective. What is the relative frequency of a CD being defective?

$$\text{Relative frequency} = \frac{\text{Number of times an outcome occurs}}{\text{Number of times the experiment is conducted}}$$

$$= \underline{\hspace{8cm}}$$

$$= \underline{\hspace{8cm}}$$

11.3 **3.** Martin tosses 2 number cubes labelled 1 to 6.
He adds the numbers showing.
He repeats the experiment 50 times.
He finds that a sum of 12 shows 3 times.

a) What is the relative frequency of a sum of 12 showing?

Express your answer as a decimal. _____

b) Suppose Martin tosses the 2 number cubes 500 times.

How many sums of 12 should he expect? _____

4. A gumball machine has these identical gumballs:
30 red, 50 blue, 20 yellow, and 40 green.

a) How many gumballs are in the machine? _____

b) A gumball comes out of the machine at random. Find each probability.
Express your answers as fractions, then as decimals rounded to 3 decimal places.

- Probability of gumball being red
- Probability of gumball being yellow

= _____

= _____

$\doteq$ _____

= _____

= _____

$\doteq$ _____

- Probability of gumball not being blue =

= _____

$\doteq$ _____

c) Suppose Jenna and Fred get 20 gumballs from the machine.
Predict how many gumballs will be red.

_____

_____

11.4 **5.** Bag A contains 1 white (W), 1 black (B),
and 1 striped (S) marble.
Bag B contains 1 white (W) and 1 black (B) marble.

Bag A   **Bag B**

a) List all possible outcomes of picking a marble
from Bag A followed by a marble from Bag B.

_____

b) What is the chance of each outcome?

- Picking 2 white marbles: _____

- Picking 1 white and 1 black marble: _____

- Picking 2 striped marbles: _____